KU-166-652

TELL ME A STORY

Over 50 specially chosen stories, poems and activities for boys and girls aged 3-6

Taken from "The People's Friend" Children's Corner,
the ever-popular regular page for readers and their little ones
in one of Britain's top-selling weekly magazines

Printed and Published in Great Britain by D.C. Thomson & Co., Ltd., Dundee, Glasgow and London.
© D.C. Thomson & Co., Ltd., 2008. ISBN 978-1-84535-365-0   EAN 9 781845 353650

WHAT'S INSIDE

POEMS

STORIES

My Tree House

IN the garden,
Daddy made
A tree house just
for me,
And when I'm there
I like to think
I'm on a ship,
at sea.

········· 🐾 ·········

I wear my big, black
rubber boots,
My woolly bobble hat,
And sail out on the
waves so high,
With Tiger Tim, my cat.

········· 🐾 ·········

I'm lost at sea for
days and days,
And then see land
ahead.
Or else I build myself
a nest
And I'm a bird,
instead.

Other ships may pass
me by.
I wave to them, and shout,
"Be careful of the
dangerous rocks!
Don't swim! There's
sharks about!"

········· 🐾 ·········

Sometimes, when the
wind is rough,
It gives me quite a fright,
And Tiger Tim, he says
to me,
"You'd better hold
on tight!"

········· 🐾 ·········

I think that I am
Robin Hood,
Up there amongst
the trees,
"Look, there's the sheriff
with his men.
Keep still! Keep quiet!
Don't sneeze!"

I pretend I'm in
the jungle,
High up where
monkeys go;
Whilst in the distance
tigers roar,
And lions prowl
below.

········· 🐾 ·········

A dragon, once, my
tree house climbed,
All green, with
talons black;
And Tim rode bravely
on its tail
Whilst I rode on its
back.

········· 🐾 ·········

And then a witch
imprisoned us
High in our castle tower.
"Quick, Tim!" I cried.
"Let us escape,
Or we'll be in her
power!"

········· 🐾 ·········

Just then a welcome
voice we heard
We both rushed down
our tree,
And Mummy shouted,
"Come on,
Come in! It's time
for tea!"

Midget's Dream

MIDGET, the toy mouse, was feeling rather sorry for herself. You see, ever since Megan had been given Mousey, a real mouse, Midget had been left at the back of the toy cupboard.

What's more, she was hidden in a fluffy pink slipper and no-one even knew she was there! Poor Midget had to stay there all alone. At least it was warm!

Sometimes, Midget listened as Megan played with Mousey outside the toy cupboard.

"You're so lovely, Mousey," Megan would say. "I think that you're the best mouse in the whole wide world."

Before Mousey came, Megan had always told Midget that she was the best mouse in the whole wide world.

Suddenly Midget didn't feel at all special any more and a tiny tear trickled down her cheek. Now, she dreamed and hoped and wished that she was a real mouse, too.

One morning, Megan's mummy decided to do some cleaning. She got out a mop and some dusters.

"You can help me," she told Megan. "We'll begin by tidying out your messy toy cupboard."

Megan moaned under her breath. She wanted to play in the garden, not tidy her room.

Soon, though, both Megan and her mummy were busy taking all the toys out of the cupboard.

"Look inside the slipper, Mummy," Megan said. "Here's the piece of jigsaw-puzzle I couldn't find last week."

"There's something even better inside this slipper." Mummy smiled, as she held Midget Mouse out in her hand.

MIDGET, so that's where you've been hiding!" Megan cried excitedly. "I've been looking for you everywhere. I thought that I'd lost you for ever." Then she gave Midget a great big hug.

"If there are any toys you don't want now, Megan, we could give them to the charity shop down the road," Mummy said to her.

Megan thought this was a lovely idea, but Midget began to worry. She felt sure that she would be given away now that Megan had a real mouse.

But, to Midget's great joy and surprise, Megan put Midget on top of her bedside table. Although this made Midget feel quite important, she still wished she was a real mouse.

You see, she desperately wanted Megan to think she was the best mouse in the whole wide world.

However, one day, something happened which made Midget change her mind . . .

All the family were going a long way away, to another country, for their summer holiday.

AUNTY Babs will take care of Mousey for us," Mummy assured Megan, "so you won't have to worry about him at all while we're away."

"That's OK." Megan smiled. "Now that I've found Midget again, she can come with us.

"You'd like that, wouldn't you, Midget?"

Megan said, as she stroked Midget gently. "What a good thing it is that you are a toy and not real, or you wouldn't be able to come on holiday with us, either."

Midget had to agree that it was a good thing, a very good thing, indeed!

Nowadays Midget is happier than she has ever been before, and is looking forward to going away on holiday again next year with Megan and her family.

She thinks it's wonderful now that she's only a toy mouse and not a real one. In fact, she can't believe now that she ever dreamed about being real!

Spring Visitors

JENNIFER jumped out of the car and hopped from one foot to the other as she waited for Mummy to lock the car door. Then she rushed up the path between the daffodils. She loved going to visit Grandma and Grandad.

Grandma smiled as she opened the door and gave Jenny a big hug.

"Grandad's out in the garden. He's got something special to show you."

Jenny ran through the house, only stopping to give Ginger, the cat, a quick stroke, then out into the garden.

Her grandparents' garden was much bigger than the one Jenny had at home. It had a swing that had been Daddy's when he was a little boy and tall trees which, one day, Jenny would be big enough to climb.

Grandad grew lots of vegetables which Jenny loved to help pick.

Jennifer could see Grandad digging, so she crept up very quietly and shouted, "Boo!" and Grandad pretended to be frightened. It was a lovely game that they often played.

"I've got something to show you," Grandad said, taking Jenny by the hand.

He led her to the pond and, holding her tight, so she didn't fall in, he pointed to the water. Jenny frowned.

As well as all the plants that were usually growing, there was something odd floating on the top.

It was like lots of little bubbles of clear jelly, with black dots in the middle of each bubble.

"What is it, Grandad?" Jenny asked.

"Those are baby frogs — or will be soon. It's called frogspawn," Grandad explained. He let her touch the jelly stuff very gently with her finger.

"See, each one of those little dots is a baby frog, and it will change, very slowly."

EACH time she visited Grandma and Grandad, Jenny also visited the frogs.

One rainy day, she went down the garden in her wellies and raincoat and nearly cried when she realised the frogspawn had all disappeared.

But Grandad grinned and explained that the tadpoles had hatched, and were swimming around in the pond.

They got a jar and Grandad fished in the water. Sure enough, when he pulled out the jar, there were lots of little black things swimming around in it.

"They're called tadpoles now," Grandad told her, as he poured them back in the pond. Grandma scolded both of them for playing out in the rain and getting wet, but Jenny was glad she had seen them.

AS the days got longer and the weather got warmer, Jenny watched the tadpoles, which were getting bigger and fatter.

"Grandad!" she shouted one day. "Look, this one's got legs!" Sure enough, little back legs had begun to grow.

The tadpoles seemed to be bigger every time Jenny came. They grew little front legs as well, but still had a tail.

She helped Grandad put some rocks in the pond and they leaned sticks against the side.

"They breathe air like you and me, now, so we have to give them a way out of the pond," Grandad explained. Jenny was disappointed. She wanted the frogs to stay.

But then, on a hot sunny day, she and Grandad crept towards the pond and there, sitting on a rock, was a proper little greeny-brown frog.

ACTIVITY

COUNT THE TADPOLES.

How many frogs will there be by spring?

As they watched, it took a huge leap and hopped off into the long grass.

"There!" said Jenny. "He's gone off exploring."

"Yes," Grandad agreed. "It's almost grown up now, but you wait — next spring it will come back and have babies of its own."

And do you know what? The very next year Jenny proudly carried a jar of frogspawn into her new school to show all the other children and tell them about the miracle of tadpoles.

ACTIVITY

POINT TO THE SPOTS ON THE DINOSAUR'S BODY.

Now find his stripes.

A LONG time ago, in a large forest, there lived a group of dinosaurs. The dinosaurs were every different shape, size and colour you could imagine. Some had stripes or spots. Some didn't.

Others had curly green whiskers, while their friends had straight blue whiskers. No two dinosaurs looked alike.

One day, one of the dinosaurs, called Dinky, woke up feeling bored.

"Nothing exciting has happened around here for ages," she said to her friend Desmond. "Why don't we organise an event all the dinosaurs can join in?"

Dinky and Desmond couldn't think of anything themselves, so they asked around for ideas.

The plan they finally agreed on was a beauty contest.

"We've never had a beauty contest before." Daisy Dinosaur smiled. "I can't wait. I might even win first prize. My purple and green spots are so attractive."

Some of the blue-and-yellow-spotted dinosaurs snorted in disagreement.

"Yuk!" they said. "Purple and green, how awful!"

Then, some of the striped dinosaurs said they thought all spots looked terrible!

"Stripes are much more tasteful!" they said.

"Yes," Dudley, a checked dinosaur, agreed. "And checks look even better."

12

Dinosaurs in Disguise

As the day of the beauty contest grew nearer, there was more and more squabbling amongst the dinosaurs. Each of them thought that they should win.

SOON, old friends weren't talking to each other. No-one could agree on anything.

"This isn't what I planned at all!" Dinky sighed to Desmond. "We're supposed to be having fun — not arguments."

"I know," Desmond replied, thoughtfully. "I'm dreading the beauty contest tomorrow. But, wait a minute, I think I've got a plan that will solve everything."

Desmond whispered his idea to Dinky. She couldn't help laughing at it.

"You're so clever, Desmond." She smiled. "Let's get ready at once!"

That evening, all the dinosaurs went to bed early to catch up on their beauty sleep. Some slept with their whiskers in curlers. Others dabbed beauty cream on their spots or stripes. They all wanted to look their best for the big day.

As soon as everyone else was asleep, Dinky and Desmond got up.

"Quickly, Dinky," Desmond whispered. "Get the paints and brushes. We've got work to do."

Desmond and Dinky crept amongst the snoring dinosaurs and began to paint them. They splashed spots on the stripy dinosaurs and painted checks on the spotted ones!

On the pink and orange dinosaurs, they added splodges of blue and green, and to some dinosaurs they added bits of everything!

By morning, all the dinosaurs had bits of each colour and marking.

They were surprised when they woke up and discovered what had happened.

"I thought I hated spots!" Dudley said, admiring his new look. "But — wow! They look great!"

"I detested stripes," said another dinosaur. "But I love my new stripy tail."

All the dinosaurs felt the same way and, suddenly, they realised just how silly they had been.

"We've all found out that it doesn't matter whether you have spots, stripes or what colour you are — we all look lovely — and we don't need a beauty contest to prove it!" said Dudley.

Dinky and Desmond breathed a sigh of relief. Their plan had worked. Everyone was friends again.

Then the dinosaurs decided to hold the beauty contest, just for fun. And each one of them won a prize — a prehistoric pineapple!

Afterwards they had a big party to celebrate. And they all went home feeling very happy.

Harry's Birthday Present

HARRY heard a chug! chug! noise and looked out of his bedroom window. A tractor was coming up the road, pulling a cart filled with logs. He ran downstairs.

"Mummy, Mummy!" he shouted. "It's Farmer Geoff and his tractor!"

"Oh, good!" Mummy said. "We need some logs for the fire. Three sacks will do."

She opened the front door just as Farmer Geoff stopped his tractor outside.

Harry ran out to meet him. "Now then, Harry," Farmer Geoff said. "How many sacks do you want today?"

"Three, please," Harry replied.

While Farmer Geoff carried three sacks of logs into the garage, Harry looked at his tractor. He thought it was the best tractor he'd ever seen. It had massive wheels at the back and a seat high up behind the windscreen. Harry wished he could drive it.

He liked it so much that when Mummy and Daddy asked him what he wanted for his birthday, he said a tractor, like Farmer Geoff's.

"That might be a problem," Daddy said. "It wouldn't fit in the garage, never mind your bedroom."

"What about some roller-skates?" Mummy asked.

"Roller-skates can't carry things like logs," Harry replied.

HIS birthday came nearer and it didn't look as though Harry was going to get a tractor.

But, on the morning of his birthday, when he expected to find something like roller-skates, there, in his bedroom, was a little red tractor, with pedals, and a cart attached to it!

"Happy birthday!" Mummy and Daddy said together. "Do you like your tractor?"

"Yes!" Harry shouted and he jumped on to the seat and pedalled around his bedroom.

But what could he carry in his cart?

At breakfast, when Mummy opened the fridge door, she had a shock.

"We've no more milk," she cried. "Now we can't have our cereal."

"I'll go to the village shop," Daddy said. "We need some dog food for Barker and a newspaper as well."

"Can I carry them in my tractor?" Harry asked eagerly.

"We'll see if they fit in," Daddy said.

OFF Harry went on his tractor, pedalling along the pavement, followed by Daddy and Barker.

When they got to the village shop, Daddy loaded two cartons of milk and a tin of dog food into Harry's cart.

Daddy bought a newspaper and put that into the cart as well.

"Yes!" Harry shouted. "They all fit in!"

He made a noise like a tractor and pedalled off down the pavement. But everyone wanted to say "Hello!" to him.

"That's a very nice tractor, Harry," Mr McTwinny said, and his Scottie dogs barked in agreement.

Then Mrs Downy came along, with her baby in a pushchair.

"Hi, Harry!" she called. "I like your tractor!"

The baby gurgled in agreement.

But Daddy had to hurry him along.

"Come on, Harry," he said. "We haven't had our cereal yet, and Barker wants his breakfast, too."

But one last person made Harry stop on his way home. It was Farmer Geoff in his big tractor, chugging down the road.

"Now then, Harry," Farmer Geoff called out. "That's a very fine tractor you've got! What are you delivering today?"

"Some milk and dog food and a newspaper," Harry cried.

"You'll soon be taking over my job," Farmer Geoff said, with a smile and a wave, and off he chugged in his big tractor.

Harry was very happy. Everybody liked his little red tractor and, at last, he was carrying useful things in it, just like Farmer Geoff!

15

Titus

TITUS TIGER lived far away, deep in a big jungle.

He should have been very happy there. The trouble was, though, Titus thought he was the only animal in the jungle who wasn't clever.

One day, as he was padding through the jungle, Titus saw some monkeys swinging happily from branch to branch in the trees.

"Hi, Titus," they called out. "It's a lovely day for swinging in the trees. Come and join us."

"I can't swing in the trees." Titus sighed. "I'm a tiger and I'm not clever like you."

As Titus continued on his way, a hissing noise startled him.

"Watch where you're going, Titus-s-s!" A wriggly snake hissed. "You nearly trod on me."

"Sorry, but I didn't hear you slithering along the ground," Titus apologised.

"I bet you can't s-s-slither and wriggle like I can." The snake hissed.

"No, I can't," Titus said. "I'm a tiger and I'm not clever like you."

Farther along, some

16

Tiger

ACTIVITY

LET'S HEAR YOU ROAR LIKE TITUS TIGER!

Mind you don't scare your grandma!

baby elephants were in a pool, squirting water over each other with their trunks.

"Hi, Titus," they called. "It's great fun squirting water. Come and try."

"I can't squirt water!" Titus sighed. "I'm a tiger and I'm not clever like you."

Titus had padded a long way by now and felt rather weary, so he stopped to listen to some birds singing.

"Hi, Titus," they chirped. "We're singing because we're happy. Why don't you sing along with us?"

"I can't sing!" Titus sighed. "I'm a tiger and I'm not clever like you."

THEN, suddenly, the sun disappeared, and the sky became very dark.

The birds looked worried, and they all stopped singing.

"Sh-sh, we must be very quiet and listen out for the BIG storm which is coming our way," they explained.

"Run along home, Titus, and warn the other animals you meet on your way back."

Titus didn't like storms. Thunder made him jump and the bright lightning flashes scared him.

He fled.

"There's a BIG storm on its way!" Titus roared loudly when he reached the elephants to warn them. Then he did the same when he met the snake, then the monkeys, until he reached home.

NOW that he was back with his mummy and daddy, he wasn't so afraid when the wind howled, the lightning flashed and the thunder crashed.

Titus had been very brave, warning all the animals about the storm, before going home by himself.

But he still wasn't happy.

"I wish I was clever like all the other animals." He sighed.

Later that evening, as Titus was trying to get to sleep, he suddenly thought of something he could do.

"I can ROAR!" he told himself. "After all, I warned the other animals that a storm was near by ROARING. And Daddy Tiger told me the only other animal who roars is the lion, the king of the jungle. So I'm as clever as the king! I must be very clever indeed!"

It was a very happy Titus Tiger who fell fast asleep that night.

And he was just as happy when he awoke the next day, too!

17

TINA MOVES HOME

O NE sunny morning, Tina Thrush looked out from her nest in the bramble hedge, and decided it was time to move home.

I'd like to live by the river, she thought to herself. I think I'll build myself a new nest right by the riverbank.

So, humming a little tune, Tina flew off and found the perfect spot, a lovely weeping willow tree, whose branches trailed into the water.

"This is wonderful!" she chirped happily. "I'll begin searching for twigs to build my nest right away!"

Tina Thrush flew back and forth, until she had collected

a large mound of twigs.

One more trip and I'll have enough to start building, she thought. But as she returned with the last stick in her beak, the little bird had a surprise. All her nesting material had disappeared!

"How funny!" Tina said to herself, scratching her head with the stick. "Whatever can have happened to it?"

Tina searched all over the riverbank, but there wasn't one twig to be found.

Just then, a little beaver appeared.

"Hello!" said Tina in surprise.

"Hello!" Benny Beaver replied. "I haven't seen you round here before!"

Tina explained that she was moving house.

"I had collected a whole mound of twigs for my new nest," she told Benny, "but it seems to have gone!"

Benny Beaver turned red with embarrassment.

"Oh, dear!" he said. "I didn't realise they were yours. I used them to finish building my dam!"

Benny was so sorry, Tina couldn't be cross.

"Oh well." She smiled. "I can easily find more."

Off she flew to fetch some lovely soft moss and leaves. But coming back again, she found her second collection had also gone!

"Who could have taken it this time?"
She sighed.

Suddenly, Tina heard a noise. She hopped round and bumped straight into Bonnie Badger! Bonnie was carrying a large pile of leaves.

"Lovely day!" Bonnie called. "I'm making a new bed for my den. I've found a super pile of moss under the weeping willow tree!"

Poor Tina could hardly chirp a reply.

"That was mine!" she managed to say. "It was for my new nest!"

"Sorry!" Bonnie gulped. "You can have it back if you want."

Tina shook her head kindly.

"You keep it!" she said, and flew off to find some more. This time she hid her sticks in a hole under the tree. But coming back across the river, she had another shock. All her twigs were floating down the river!

THIS is puzzling." Tina sighed.

She looked in the hole under the willow tree and, to her surprise, found a mouse busily sweeping her twigs into the river.

"Morning." Molly Mouse smiled. "I'm just clearing up."

When Tina told Molly what she'd done, the mouse was sorry, especially when Bonnie and Benny arrived to add their stories.

"Perhaps we can help," Bonnie suggested. "We'll collect some sticks for you."

So Tina had a rest, while her new friends went out. Soon they had collected a huge pile but none of it was any good.

"I can't use any of this!" Tina sighed, holding up an enormous piece of bark. "It's much too big for a nest! It's a shame I can't just move my old nest to the weeping willow tree instead!" she chirped.

The three friends laughed.

"Let's do just that!" they said. So they did. Between them, they carried Tina's old nest out of the bramble hedge and into the willow tree. It was perfect!

"Thank you!" Tina laughed happily. "I know I'm going to love living here — especially with friends like you. This really is a home from home!" And she invited them all in for tea!

19

ONE day, Emma ran to Mummy, with a happy shout,
"You know I had a wobbly tooth — well, it's just fallen out!"
And Mum was pleased.
"I'll tell you what you must do," she said,
"Put it underneath your pillow, when you go to bed.
Then, in the night, when you're asleep, the Tooth Fairy will come,
And take the tooth, and leave instead, a small surprise," said Mum.

"For fairies use these tiny teeth, so nice and pearly-clean,
When building castles, gleaming white, for their Fairy Queen,"
So Emma did as Mummy said, and hid the tooth that night,
Beneath her pillow, where next morn, she found to her delight,
That the fairy must have been . . . the little tooth had gone,
While in its place a little coin, like silver, brightly shone!

Down to the kitchen Emma ran, to spread the happy news,
And found Mum making toast, while Dad was polishing his shoes.
"How lovely!" Mummy cried, and then, "It's market day today,
We'll look on Mrs Duckett's stall — she has nice toys, they say."
And later on, when Mum had bought her apples for a pie,
Emma gazed with big round eyes, wondering what to buy . . .

Emma's New Friend

A skipping rope, a
drawing book, a pretty
bouncing ball —
There were piles and
piles of things on Mrs
Duckett's stall!
But what about the
Teddy bear — he only had
one eye,
How lonely and sad he
looked, as people passed
him by!
Then kindly Mrs Duckett
saw how Emma looked
at Ted.
"If you would like that little
bear, he's going cheap,"
she said.

So Emma asked, "Is this
enough?", holding out
her hand.
"A little fairy brought me
this, last night, from
Fairyland."
"Now, fancy that!
Good gracious me!"
And Mrs Duckett smiled.
"That's just the right
amount," she said. "You
are a lucky child!"
And Emma's mummy,
once back home, found
needle and brown
thread,
To stitch a button on —
and make another eye
for Ted!

And now, he has two eyes
again, and no-one gives a jot
Whether those shining
eyes are quite the same —
or not.
For Emma loves him

very much, she takes him
everywhere,
Her favourite toy of all
— that darling little bear!

There's A Lamb In My Basket!

IT was a too-wet-to-go-out sort of day, but, in the farmhouse, Jacko, the brown dog, was warm and dry, in his comfy basket, in the cosy kitchen.

He thought he might have a sleep.

Suddenly, in came the farmer. He was carrying a lamb.

It was wet from the top of its head to the tip of its tail.

"It never rains but it pours!" said the farmer. "The fields are almost flooded, but you'll be all right indoors." He put the lamb into Jacko's basket.

"I don't want to share my basket with a lamb!" Jacko cried.

He got up and shook himself.

He went to tell the horses. By the time he reached the stables, his feet were very wet.

The horses exclaimed.

"There's a lamb in my basket and I don't know why!" he said.

"P'raps the farmer's going to have a party for all the animals," said a silly young filly.

She shook out her mane and did fancy high-step prancing.

"I must get my feet shod if there's going to be dancing," said a carthorse.

"Forget the party!" said the old grey mare. "Jacko's feet are wet. Fetch the horse blanket!"

Jacko rolled over and over on it, to get dry.

"If I were you, I wouldn't take long," said the carthorse. "That blanket has a bit of a pong."

WHEN he had thanked the horses, Jacko went to see the cows. By the time he reached the cowshed, his coat was very wet.

The cows were shocked.

"There's a lamb in my basket and I don't know why!" he said.

"P'raps the farmer suffers from absent-mindedness," said a brown cow.

"What's ab-something-ness?" her calf wanted to know.

Another cow offered to demonstrate, by jumping over the garden gate. She absent-mindedly jumped too high — right over the moon, high up in the sky.

"Forget this nonsense!" said an older cow. "Jacko's coat is wet. Get in a circle, and when I say go, all take a deep breath and blow a big blow."

The calf began to giggle and laugh.

"I'll have to blow for one and a half," said the brown cow.

"It's like a typhoon!" cried Jacko.

"You'll be dry quite soon," puffed the cows.

When he had thanked them, Jacko went to see the hens.

By the time he reached the hen-house, he was wet from the top of his head to the tip of his tail.

The hens clucked in sympathy.

"There's a lamb in my basket and I don't know why!" he said.

"P'raps the farmer thought it was a puppy," said the hens. "They both have four legs and a tail — it's easy to make a mistake."

"I once thought some rope was a snake," cheeped a chick.

"Quiet everyone, please!" said a little red hen. "Jacko is wet through!"

"Come in," said the hens. "We'll try to make some room for you."

It was rather a squash. Jacko couldn't even shake himself. He longed for his comfy basket in the cosy kitchen. He thought for a while.

THERE's a lamb in my basket and now I know why!" he said suddenly. "The farmer put him in there, to keep warm and dry."

He thanked the hens and hurried home.

"You can share my basket," he told the lamb. "There's room for you — there's room for two."

They settled down, side by side, and soon they were warm as toast and dry right down to their tails, and it wasn't long before they became the best of friends.

23

SPRING was just around the corner and Bob, the robin, was very excited.

He was to join in the singing in the garden birds' dawn chorus.

But, the previous autumn, he had packed away the fine, new red waistcoat he had planned to wear, and now he couldn't remember where it was.

While searching, he met Spreckle, the thrush, who was in a similar plight.

"I've lost some songs," she warbled. "I'm sure I put them somewhere safe!"

The two of them searched for ages and found nothing. At last Bob had an idea.

"Let's ask Great-uncle Sagacity," he chirped. "Maybe he'll be able to help."

Off they went, to the top of the garden, where old Great-uncle Sagacity, who was an exceptionally wise toad, lived under a broken flower pot.

"Can you help us, please?" Bob asked. "Spreckle has lost some songs and I can't find my new red waistcoat!"

"Hum," Great-uncle Sagacity croaked. "I do see the difficulty. That east wind this winter shifted everything. Everybody seems to have lost something, even the snails, and them so slow and careful!

"We could . . . hum . . . we'll call a meeting! Ask everybody you meet to gather here tomorrow morning."

THE next day everybody arrived to see what was happening.

Great-uncle Sagacity sat on the top of his flowerpot.

"If you all agree," he announced, "we're going to have a treasure hunt to find all the things we've lost.

The Treasure Hunt

We'll all meet here at noon with whatever we've found."

Everybody set off full of enthusiasm.

The snails and spiders crawled up the walls to look in the cracks; the frogs and newts did an underwater survey of the pond; the birds turned over all the old leaves in the shrubbery and flew around the trees.

NEVER had there been such scuffling, shuffling, digging, delving, peering and probing in the garden.

It was very interesting, especially when somebody chirped, croaked or squawked that they'd found something and everybody nearby rushed to see what it was.

By noon, a huge pile had gathered.

There was Peg the magpie's silver paper collection, Hector squirrel's giant pine cone (a family heirloom), wee woodmouse's lucky acorn and all the lovely bits of string which Mrs Chaffinch liked to use in her nest. There was the golden shell awarded to the winner of the snails' annual wall race and dozens of other things besides.

It was such a success that some things were found which had been lost for so long that everybody had forgotten all about them.

BOB, the robin, was delighted when his waistcoat turned up.

Wee woodmouse had found it in the potting shed.

Bob joyfully tugged it out of the pile.

"It still fits, too. Thank you, wee woodmouse!"

Spreckle's songs turned up – Hector, the squirrel, discovered them packed away safely in a hollow hazel nut.

"The songs!" Spreckle trilled, "Oh, I am glad. I really thought they were lost for ever."

The garden fairly rang with happy exclamations as everybody was re-united with bits of lost property.

"The treasure hunt is the best idea you've ever had, Great-uncle Sagacity," Spreckle said.

"We should have one every year!" declared Great-uncle Sagacity.

"Oh, yes! Definitely!"

They all agreed it was a wonderful idea, especially Spreckle, the thrush, and Bob, the robin, who was all ready for the dawn chorus in his fine, red waistcoat.

Archie and the Spring-cleaning

ARCHIE, the farm cat, liked to take an occasional nap in the tractor shed, which was where all the clutter of the farm landed; everything from bits of odd implements, spare parts, tools, boxes, old paint tins . . . all sorts of things, just heaped up, here and there.

It was really a very interesting place to rummage in, even if, at times, there was hardly any room for the tractor.

In the midst of all the odds and ends, Archie had his own cushion which sat on the top of a tea-chest. Once it had been rather a grand sofa cushion; now it was worn and saggy, but still very comfy.

One day, Archie decided to take his nap, as usual, but when he reached the shed, he hardly recognised it. It was tidy! Archie gasped and looked round and round.

All the implements had been tidied, the tools were hanging up neatly in rows and the boxes were all stacked.

"I can't see my cushion!" He miaowed. He sped off to see if Trim, the collie, knew anything about what was happening.

"The shed is tidy, Trim!" Archie said. "I can't find my cushion and I don't know where to look for it. Whatever's been happening?"

Trim pricked up her ears, looking very surprised.

"It's spring-cleaning, Archie. Farmer MacDonald said he'd spring-clean the shed, because it was full of rubbish."

"My cushion — rubbish!" spluttered Archie with a snuffle of his whiskers. "Throwing out comfy cushions can't be the proper way to spring-clean. I think I'll lend a paw to help, just to make sure that nothing else has been thrown out which shouldn't have been."

Archie soon saw his cushion. There it was, on top of the tea-chest, which was on top of a pile of bin bags.

"I'll jump up and get it," he mewed. "Then I'll look through the rest."

"Be careful!" Trim barked.

Archie jumped, but not far enough. He just caught the corner of the cushion.

"Mee-eee-ooow!" Archie wailed, as the cushion toppled off the tea-chest, causing it to topple, too!

Crash! The tea-chest fell over, spilling all sorts of things of every description, including Archie and his cushion, all over the farmyard.

"Oh, what a mess I've made," he moaned.

FARMER MACDONALD came out to see what had caused such a clatter. Archie was just about to explain about his cushion, when Farmer MacDonald spotted something.

"A box of nails and that spanner I lost!" he exclaimed. "If I'd known that was in the old tea-chest, I'd

never have thrown it out. I thought it was full of junk!"

"There's my spare collar." Trim barked. "It's been lost for ages."

Jock, the terrier, joined in, too.

"Here's my rubber bone!"

"Here are some paint brushes," said Farmer MacDonald. "To think I nearly bought new ones."

"Look at all this string!" Mrs MacDonald exclaimed. "And these flower pots; just what I was looking for!"

Soon they had gathered up all the handy things which had lain forgotten in the old tea-chest.

"We'll just put that tea-chest back where it was. It holds so much and that cushion is just like a lid," Farmer MacDonald said, looking very pleased.

"It's a good thing you helped out with the spring-cleaning, Archie," said Mrs MacDonald, as she stroked Archie's head, "or else we would have thrown out all these useful things!"

Archie purred. He was very pleased and quite surprised at the way things had turned out.

Not only had he got his good old cushion back, but he had discovered a talent he didn't know he had — he was good at spring-cleaning! Not many cats could say that.

27

Harold the Dreamer

HAROLD is a brown bunny with a twitchy nose, floppy ears and a fluffy tail. He is a good little bunny, and is always cheerful and very polite. Unfortunately, Harold is a dreamer. He's always thinking about something and dreaming instead of doing what he actually should be doing.

Sometimes, Harold's dreaming gets him into trouble. On the way to bunny school one day, Harold looked up at the sky. He watched the fluffy white clouds floating lazily by. The clouds were sails on

28

tall ships. The sky was the deep, blue sea.

Harold dreamed that he was a brave captain, sailing his ship to far off lands. He dreamed of an island and buried treasure — gold and silver and precious jewels.

While Harold dreamed about the sea, the clouds changed shape. Now they were elephants charging across the sky, their long trunks swinging from side to side.

Harold was just thinking how funny it would be if his nose was as long as an elephant's trunk, when he heard the school bell ringing. He was late!

"Dreaming again, Harold?" the teacher would say, and all the other little bunnies would laugh.

WHEN Harold wasn't at school, he helped the other bunnies make eggs for Easter. Harold's job was to stir the big pot of chocolate. Harold tried really hard to keep his mind on what he was doing. He tried to keep his dreaming for bedtime, but it wasn't easy. Why can't chickens lay chocolate eggs, Harold thought as he stirred the chocolate. If the farmer fed them chocolate instead of corn maybe they could . . .

The chocolate bubbled away as Harold dreamed. It bubbled higher and higher in the big pot. Then it spilled over the side and made chocolate puddles on the floor.

Grandfather Bunny was cross.

"Dreaming again, Harold?" he asked and he sent Harold off to do something else.

Harold's new job was to dip the marshmallow eggs into the warm, runny chocolate, then put them on a table to cool. Harold dipped an egg into the chocolate. How yummy it looked!

Harold dipped another egg. He drew a wavy line in the soft chocolate. He drew another line. And another!

The lines were ocean waves breaking on the sand — tiny waves, all cool and tingly that tickle your toes. Harold put the wavy egg on the table.

ON the next egg, he made zig-zaggy lines, then dots and crosses. Harold was having fun. He did squiggly lines and wiggly lines; he drew moons and stars; he made swirls and curls. How wonderful the eggs looked.

Grandfather Bunny came over to inspect the eggs. He picked one up and turned it this way and that. Harold held his breath. Would Grandfather Bunny be cross?

Grandfather Bunny was smiling.

"I see you've been dreaming again, Harold," he said.

"I dreamed all the patterns," Harold said proudly, and all the other bunnies crowded around to see what he had done.

Grandmother Bunny gave Harold a big bunny hug.

"You really are a clever little bunny," she said. "What ever will you dream up next?"

But Harold wasn't listening. He was dreaming of wonderful Easter eggs — special eggs — wrapped in gold and silver paper, eggs with fluffy yellow chickens or bows on top.

Harold smiled to himself. He was thinking of all the happy children who would find the eggs on Easter morning.

If you find an egg on Easter morning, more wonderful than any you have ever seen before, you will know that it is one of Harold the Dreamer's special Easter eggs.

DAISY DUCK

YOUNG Daisy Duck was very vain. She loved herself like mad. She stared at her reflection In the pond each chance she had.

She preened her feathers all the time And looked down at her face. Twin brother Dan thought Daisy strange, And quacked, "You're a nut case!"

"But I can't swim,"
young Daisy cried.
"I'll sink right down,
I'm sure."
She preened her feathers
once again
And loved herself once more.

One night the ducks were
fast asleep
When wind howled loud
and clear.
The lightning flashed and
thunder crashed
As a big storm drew near.

Next morning Daisy
waddled off
To see her face again.
But now the pond was full
of twigs
And leaves. She searched
in vain.

"The water is so dirty!"
Daisy sighed, quite close
to tears.
"Perhaps I'll never see
my face
Again for years and years."

Just then she saw a
floating branch
And so she jumped on top,
And, as the branch went
round and round,
She searched again,
non-stop.

Down at the end, the
pond was clean.
At last Daisy could see
Her very own reflection
And she quacked, "Down
there, it's ME!"

And then, before she'd
stopped to think,
She jumped SPLASH! in
the pond,
To pick up her reflection
Of which she'd grown
so fond.

But Daisy wasn't
quick enough!
She didn't catch a thing.
But now it didn't
matter, for
She'd taught herself
to swim!

The other ducks all
quacked, "Well done!"
When they saw Daisy swim.
"This is such fun."
Proud Daisy smiled.
"Why don't you all
come in?"

Then Daisy swam each
day until
She beat Dan in a race.
"Your swimming has
improved a lot!"
Dan grinned. "More
than your face!"

"Now, Dan, that wasn't
very nice,
Say sorry," quacked
their mummy.
But Dan swam to the
other side
And floated on his
tummy.

"It's time you learned to
swim, Daisy,"
Mummy Duck said one day.
"Your brother now wins
every race.
Come in the pond
and play."

HAMMOND VERY BIG

HAMMOND BEAR wanted to play. But Jessica was at school and his big teddy bear friend, Rebus, was snoozing.

"Rebus, wake up. Play with me, please," Hammond said, shaking Rebus by the arm.

Rebus opened his eyes.

"Little Hammond Bear, you're being a pest. I'm older than you, I need my rest." And with that Rebus closed his eyes again.

Hammond couldn't help smiling. Rebus always talked in verse.

But then Hammond frowned. He still had no one to play with.

I'll just have to play on my own, he thought.

HAMMOND moved to the edge of the bed and slid down the duvet. He started to go over to Jessica's toy corner when he noticed the bedroom door was open. Usually it was firmly closed.

Aha! Hammond thought, a chance to explore. He put his paw round the door and swung it open. He looked back at Rebus but he was still fast asleep. Hammond went out on to the landing. Jessica's father was at work and her mother was visiting a friend.

BEAR'S PHEW!

How exciting. He chuckled to himself.

Hammond went to the top of the stairs. He looked up at the brightly polished banister rail running all the way downstairs, curving at the bottom.

That looks like it would be fun to slide on, Hammond decided. And climbing up the knobbly post, he sat astride the banister. Then, raising his arms in the air, he slid all the way to the bottom!

"Wheeeee! What fun!" he cried, as he went down at speed.

THE little bear climbed off, laughing, wanting to do it again and again. But when he got to the bottom of the stairs, he realised they were rather steep for a little bear. To get on to the first step he had to swing his leg up and pull himself up with both paws. It was very hard work.

Looking up, Hammond could see that he had a lot of stairs to climb. But what would Jessica say if she found him at the bottom of the stairs when she came home from school?

Hammond Bear loved Jessica and didn't want to worry her.

Pulling his shoulders back and taking a deep breath, Hammond started the slow climb up the stairs.

It took a very long time but at last Hammond made it. He lay down on the top step, absolutely exhausted.

Then with the last of his strength he got up and went back into the bedroom. He pulled himself up on the duvet and lay on the bed.

"Phew!" Hammond said, panting. "That was a Very Big Phew."

Rebus stirred. Hammond moved over to him and laid his head on Rebus's rather large tummy. It was very comfortable.

Hammond felt Rebus pat him gently as he fell asleep.

HAMMOND woke up to see Jessica at the side of the bed, smiling down at them both.

"What lovely bears you two are. I really miss you when I'm at school. But now we can all play together," she said, as she went to change

her school uniform.

When Jessica came back to the bed to play Hammond hoped she wouldn't notice that he was still rather tired.

Jessica picked him up and took hold of Rebus's paw.

"I hope you two don't get too bored while I'm at school," she said.

Rebus chuckled.

"I think if Jessica only knew, it would be an even bigger Phew."

As he snuggled up to Jessica, Hammond Bear had to admit Rebus was right. I'll play in the bedroom in future, he decided.

And no more Very Big Phews, Hammond promised himself, as Jessica took them to her toy corner for one of the exciting games they played together every day.

33

A Fishy Tale

A **LITTLE** fish lived among some weeds in a cave near the bottom of the sea.

He liked his home and was very happy, but he also had a great desire to go exploring.

"Never swim past the giant, jagged rock," his mother warned him. "It isn't safe."

The little fish swam down to the sea bed instead, where he saw fish of every size and shape and colour.

"It's lovely here," the little fish said. "I wonder what it's like on the surface."

The little fish swam up to the surface of the sea. As he popped his head out of the water to look around, a gull swooped down and scooped him up with her beak.

High, high into the air they went.

"Help!" the little fish shouted. "I don't want to be eaten by a gull!"

He wriggled so much that he slipped out of the gull's beak. Down, down he fell until — SPLASH! — the little fish landed safely in the water and swam away.

"Where are you going, little fish?" some crabs shouted.

"I'm exploring," the little fish said proudly.

"Well, don't swim past the giant, jagged rock," they warned.

The little fish swam on. It was very exciting. He saw jellyfish, lobsters, whales, dolphins and eels.

This is beautiful, he thought. I'm so glad I came exploring. What a lot of things I'll have to tell my mother when I get home.

"Hello, little fish. What are you doing?" a passing seahorse asked.

"I'm exploring."

"Well, turn around and swim home," the seahorse said. "Because over there is the giant, jagged rock. It's not safe to swim past that."

The little fish looked towards the giant, jagged rock. He had never seen it before.

"It's enormous!" he cried. "What's that creature on the other side of it? I've never seen anything like that before."

"That's a swordfish," the seahorse replied. "Little fish, where are you going? Come back!"

THE little fish wasn't listening. He forgot all of the warnings he had been given and went to take a closer look at the swordfish.

Unfortunately, the swordfish swam so fast that the little fish couldn't keep up with him.

"What's that?" The little fish paused as he caught sight of a strange shape.

He swam down into the

murky depths and saw a battered shipwreck. He went closer to investigate.

"What are you doing here?" the octopus who lived in the shipwreck asked. "It's not safe for fish to swim past the giant, jagged rock. Go home."

IT was only then that the little fish remembered all of the warnings he had been given. He turned around and began to swim home, but it was too late.

"Help!" he shouted. "What's happening to me?"

The little fish was caught in a fisherman's net with lots of other fish. They were bigger than him and they were all trapped in the net being pulled up to the surface.

"I don't want to go up there!" he shouted. "There's a gull up there who wants to eat me!"

The little fish tried desperately to squeeze through one of the small holes in the net.

He wriggled and wriggled until . . .

"I'M FREE!" he shouted. "It's a good thing that I'm not very big."

Then he quickly swam past the giant, jagged rock, past the seahorses, eels, dolphins, whales, lobsters, jellyfish and crabs, and past the fish of every size and shape and colour.

What a lot of things I have to tell my mother, he thought as he arrived safely home.

But I won't tell her today. I need a rest after all that exploring.

And the little fish closed his eyes and went to sleep among the weeds in the cave near the bottom of the sea.

ACTIVITY

CAN YOU COUNT ALL THE LITTLE BLUE FISH SWIMMING IN THE SEA?

EWAN'S SLIPPERS

ACTIVITY

CAN YOU SEE JUST WHAT'S WRONG WITH EWAN'S YELLOW SLIPPERS?

EWAN loved his cosy yellow slippers — even though they had a bit of a hole in one toe, the pattern of red Teddies had faded almost to nothing and they were getting rather tight! So tight that Mummy had to wriggle his toes into them.

Daddy could not manage to get Ewan's feet inside the slippers at all.

"Nothing else for it!" Daddy said. "We must go and buy you some bigger slippers today!"

"Oh, dear," Mummy said. "I'm afraid Ewan and I can't come shopping today. We promised to help Izzie's mummy get ready."

Ewan forgot all about his slippers. Izzie was his best friend and he was looking forward to her birthday party.

Ewan couldn't wait to get home and tell Daddy all about the party and the fairy castle birthday cake with four candles.

But Daddy had something for Ewan — a dark blue box.

"It's not my birthday, Dad!" Ewan chuckled, but he snapped off the lid.

Inside was a pair of dark blue slippers. Plain slippers. Not a Teddy in sight.

Ewan's smile disappeared. Mummy whipped off his trainers and pulled the new slippers over his toes.

"Very smart!" Daddy said.

"A perfect fit," Mummy said. "Try walking about in them, darling. Do they feel all right?"

Ewan could not help himself — he burst into tears. The new slippers were stiff

36

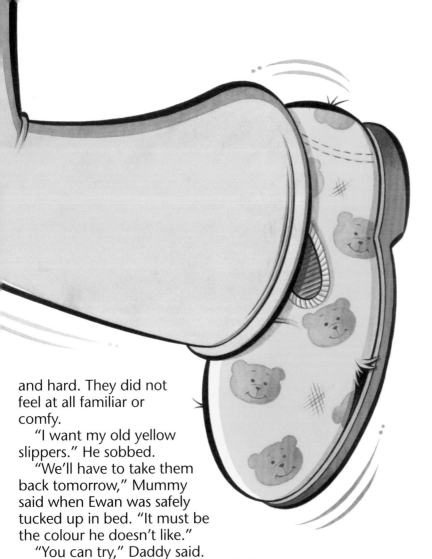

and hard. They did not feel at all familiar or comfy.

"I want my old yellow slippers." He sobbed.

"We'll have to take them back tomorrow," Mummy said when Ewan was safely tucked up in bed. "It must be the colour he doesn't like."

"You can try," Daddy said. "But I couldn't find a yellow pair in his size in any of the shops."

"Nothing else for it, then," Mummy said. "I shall have to pop out and get him some new pyjamas in dark blue to match the slippers."

But, try as he might, Ewan could not like his new slippers, even though the new pyjamas were cute — dark blue with silver spacemen — and even though his best friend, Izzie, came for a sleepover and admired his night attire, slippers and all.

NOTHING else for it," Daddy said when the two friends were snoring away happily in their bunks. "I shall have to paint Ewan's room blue to get him used to the colour."

But Ewan simply could not bring himself to like his new slippers — even though his bedroom walls looked splendid in dark blue with white clouds and silver spaceships, and even though there was a letter from Grandad to say he would be coming for a visit.

Grandad's visits were few and far between and Ewan was usually very excited to see him. He was such fun and so clever — he seemed to know everything there was to know.

Ewan woke to the sound of a deep booming voice.

"Where's my little man? I can't wait to see how much he's grown!"

EWAN raced downstairs in bare feet but, even without his shoes, he was thrilled to discover that he now came up to Grandad's middle.

But soon Grandad was swinging him off his feet and covering his face with kisses.

"Why — he's no longer my little man!" he declared. "You are practically a full-grown fellow like your old grandad! Come and help me unpack."

This was something he always said and Ewan knew there would be a surprise present on top of Grandad's clothes in his suitcase. He led the way upstairs.

Grandad flung his case on the bed and flipped open the locks. Ewan lifted up the lid and gasped. There was indeed a surprise on top — a square packet wrapped in scarlet paper — and Grandad's slippers. Grandad's dark blue slippers.

"An excellent colour for we men, eh?" Grandad said with a big wink.

Ewan ran off to fetch his new blue slippers without even waiting to unwrap his Grandad's gift.

37

Playtime Parade

A BIG parade came
to our town
But soon the
raindrops pelted down.
All of us ran
helter-skelter
Running to our homes
for shelter.

It doesn't matter if
it pours,
I have my own parade
indoors.
My toy-shelf friends all
form a band,
The music is so loud
and grand.

I am the leader of
the toys,
Marching, making
lots of noise.
When we're tired,
we'll sit down plop,
Waiting for the rain to
stop.

Duck's guitar begins
to strum,
Bear beats bang-clang
on his drum.
Elephant stomps his
great big feet
To the thump-thump,
rat-tat beat.

Clown is humming,
grinning, giggling,
Floppy arms and legs
all jiggling.
Lion growls and roars a tune
Loud enough to reach
the moon.

Cat beats time with
his long tail,
Sings a shivery, quivery wail.
Rabbit has a horn to blow,
Root-toot-tooting in
the show.

Parrot squawks and
makes a fuss
Louder than the rest of us.
Monkey watches from
his chair.
His chitter-chatter fills the air.

We all sing
dancy-prancy songs,
Jazzy, razz-matazzy songs,
Willy-nilly, silly songs
Happy, snappy, clappy songs!

Suddenly the sun comes out.
"Let's all go out to play,"
I shout.
"We'll have a toy parade again
Next time we're hiding
from the rain."

The Houseboat

RACHEL and her little brother, Josh, had recently moved into a most unusual home. Their parents had bought a large houseboat on the river.

"There's so much to do and see on the river!" Rachel had cried on first seeing their new home. "It's beautiful."

"We'll be able to go fishing every evening after school," Josh had added. "And on hot days we can even go swimming!"

That summer and autumn they had had a fantastic time. During the summer holidays they had invited their friends over for swimming parties and fishing days.

And, in the autumn, they went blackberry picking along the riverbank and helped to paint the boat.

But now it was midwinter. It was snowing and the river had half frozen over. Everything seemed so bleak and quiet.

"What are we going to do every day?" Rachel said to her mother one morning at breakfast.

"Well, you do still have school to go to," her mother reminded her.

The small village school was a walk and a bus ride away.

"Anyway," Mother continued, "you and Josh will soon find a new hobby."

RACHEL and Josh hurried to get ready for school. As they set off down the tow path and across the field to the bus stop, Rachel couldn't help noticing that there seemed to be a lot of ducks and geese standing on the canal bank. They didn't look very happy.

"They must be hungry, poor things!" Josh said. "They won't be able to find anything to eat through all the ice."

"I've got an idea!" Rachel said. "Let's look after all the animals and birds living here through the winter."

So, that's how it all began. That afternoon, when they got back, Josh and Rachel begged their mother for scraps for the hungry birds and they mixed up nuts and seeds with fat and made bird cakes.

The creatures soon became used to their regular feeds in the mornings and afternoons. They were joined by more birds, and even some unusual ones came.

"I'm going to start making a record of all the different birds I see," Josh said excitedly. "I can use it for my school nature project."

"You could do drawings of them, too," Rachel added. "We can watch them through the boat windows."

When Josh took his project to school, all his class-mates wanted to come and see the birds being fed! So Rachel and Josh invited them all to the houseboat for "nature" parties.

Then, one very snowy day, Josh and Rachel had a surprise. A rather timid badger visited the canal bank for a share of the food.

THE children were so excited!

"I've never seen a badger so close," Josh exclaimed.

"I'm sure there must be more around," Dad said. "I've seen plenty of badger prints in the snow!"

"We'll have to leave out more food for them," Rachel said. "I wonder what badgers eat?"

Josh hurried upstairs to look in his animal books.

Just then their mother called out that supper was ready.

"Oh, do we have to come now?" Josh cried. "We have so much to do!"

Suddenly, he and Rachel caught each other's eye and they giggled. To think they'd been worried about being bored through the winter. Now it seemed they'd hardly have time to fit everything in before spring arrived.

ACTIVITY

RACHEL AND JOSH LIKE TO WATCH THE BIRDS!

Can you name 4 different birds?

41

ERNIE, the earthworm, lived next to a football pitch, which was great for Ernie, as he loved football.

He had a cosy burrow in the mud under the earth and, when he heard a football match begin, he would poke his head out to watch the action.

He would get quite excited cheering on the local team, and when they scored, he would almost jump out of his burrow.

The worm who lived next door to Ernie was called Ron, and he did not like the noisy football matches at all.

"All that shouting and whistle blowing," he would grumble. "It disturbs my afternoon nap."

One afternoon, there was a very exciting game being played.

Ernie was hoarse with cheering!

Ron poked his head out of his burrow.

"Ernie, please be quiet! I'm trying to sleep," he said crossly.

"But we're winning!" Ernie cried, wiggling up and down. "Stay and watch, Ron, it's so exciting!"

Ron frowned, but he crawled out of his burrow and even shouted, "Hooray!" when a goal was scored.

Then the final whistle blew and there was a great big cheer — the home team had won!

"Wasn't that a brilliant match?" Ernie said.

"Well, it was quite good,"

ERNIE'S FOOTBALL TEAM

Ron replied, "but look at all the mess." And he flicked at a little ball of screwed-up paper that somebody had dropped.

Ernie's eyes lit up as the ball of paper rolled towards him, and he knocked it back to Ron with a neat flick of his tail.

"Wow! A football," he said and the two little worms began to pass the paper ball between them.

"That was fun!" Ernie said. "Let's have another game tomorrow."

AFTER that, the two friends often met up for a kick-about, or should we say flick-about, with the paper ball.

Sometimes their friends would join in, too. Pete Stag Beetle was great at scoring goals. And Shona Snail was a very good goalkeeper, because she could stretch herself out a lot.

One day, there were eleven of them playing.

"There's enough of us now for a real football team," Ernie said eagerly.

"Wendy Woodlouse runs a football team," Shona said. "Perhaps we should arrange a game with her?"

Ernie thought this was a jolly good idea. And so, one Sunday evening, he made his way across the football pitch and found Wendy.

She was in the middle of some very strenuous training with her team. Ernie explained why he'd come, and Wendy was very keen to organise a game between the two sides.

"What about next Sunday?" she asked.

"Er, all right," Ernie said.

When he got back, he went to see Ron.

"They look a brilliant team," Ernie sighed. "We're sure to lose, even if we train really hard!"

"But it doesn't matter if we don't win," said Ron. "It'll be fun, and we'll try our very best to play well."

SO, they practised all week and soon the big day arrived. Both teams played very well and everyone really enjoyed themselves.

And, to their surprise, Ernie's team won!

"Well done!" Wendy said. "Shall we have another match next week?"

"Yes, let's!" Ernie was delighted.

And, from then on, the two teams played football together every Sunday.

Sometimes Ernie's team won and sometimes Wendy's team won. But they always had lots of fun!

the Raggedy Man

waistcoat was made from a duster. Can you guess where his hat came from?"

Jonathan saw that his hat was made from his old tartan pyjamas. He was certainly a very special home-made toy.

One washing day, Mummy scooped up Jonathan's bedclothes and put them in the washing machine.

No-one knew that Raggedy Man had been scooped up, too, along with the duvet cover.

In the washing machine, Raggedy Man found himself being whizzed and whirled round and round in the sudsy, soapy water.

Next thing he knew, he was being taken out of the washing machine along with the damp bedclothes.

ONCE upon a time, not so long ago, there was a mummy who made a special present for her small son, Jonathan. It was a little Raggedy Man. Jonathan loved his Raggedy Man very much.

"Where did he come from, Mummy?" Jonathan asked.

"Well, now," Mummy said. "He came out of my rag-bag. I made him from all the bits of wool and material I've collected over the years.

"His check trousers were made from an old jacket of Daddy's. His yellow

This time he was hidden inside a pillow-case.

WHEN Mummy took the washing outside, she never even noticed when Raggedy Man plopped out of the pillow-case and landed on the grass.

He was just wondering what would happen next when — whoosh! — he was flying!

A big black bird had scooped him up in his beak and Raggedy Man was going higher and higher.

He saw the garden below and Mummy still hanging out the washing. Everything looked very small and very far away.

Then — flop! — the big black bird dropped him into a nest built in the tallest tree top.

Inside the nest were lots of tiny birds cheeping and chirping.

Raggedy Man peeped over the side of the nest and wondered what would happen next!

Whee . . . He was tumbling down through the leaves and branches. Down, down he went until . . . Bump! Raggedy Man had landed on the roof of the shed.

Before he even had time to wonder what would happen next, he was blown off the roof by a gust of wind. Over and over he went until he landed with a splash in Jonathan's paddling pool. Goodness me, two washes in one day!

At that moment, Jonathan came out to play.

"How did you get in there, Raggedy Man?" he asked. "I've been searching for you all day."

Carefully, Jonathan picked him out of the water and took him inside to dry by the radiator.

Raggedy Man had enjoyed his adventures in the garden, but he was glad to be back, warm and dry, in the cosy bedclothes.

Jonathan was telling him a story about the day he lost his Raggedy Man and found him again.

And soon, they were both fast asleep.

Goodnight, Jonathan. Goodnight, Raggedy Man.

45

WALTER THE WOODPECKER

WALTER, the woodpecker, was looking for a nice, friendly forest where he could hammer with his beak on tree trunks, without getting lots of complaints from its inhabitants.

The last forest he'd visited was a really beautiful place, but every time he started hammering, some creature had complained!

So he'd had no choice but to leave.

Flying high above the countryside, Walter eventually came to a fine-looking forest, so he flew down to take a closer look. There were oak, ash and chestnut trees there, all ideal for hammering on.

Seeing a particularly grand old oak, Walter couldn't resist getting to work on its trunk straight away.

Tap, tap, tap, Walter's beak drilled into the oak's gnarled trunk.

He'd only been there for a few moments, when he felt a shudder run down the tree's trunk and saw its canopy of green leaves angrily rustling above him.

"Stop that awful hammering this instant. You're giving me a headache!" the ancient oak boomed down at Walter.

"Sorry," Walter stammered. "I didn't realise I was upsetting you."

"Well, you are! So, be a good woodpecker and play somewhere else," the oak said.

WALTER obligingly flew off to a nearby chestnut tree and began hammering on its trunk, hoping for better luck this time.

"Stop that terrible noise this instant," an angry squirrel yelled down from the tree's branches. "I've a drey full of baby squirrels here and you're upsetting them."

"I'm sorry. I didn't realise this tree was occupied," Walter apologised.

He took off into the air once more, searching for another attractive tree which might be good to hammer on.

Seeing a beautiful ash, he decided to try out its trunk with his sharp beak.

Walter began to hammer, very softly and quietly at first, but soon he began to tap harder and harder.

"Too-whit-too-whoo. Who are you and why are you making so much noise below my perch? I need a good day's sleep, so I'll be refreshed for hunting tonight," a sleepy-eyed owl hooted down at Walter.

"I'm very sorry. I didn't notice you perching up there. I'll find another tree to hammer on," Walter replied.

"Yes, please do, and make it at least a mile away from here, will you?" the owl hooted.

WALTER went in search of trees at the forest's edge. It was then he spied a little group of silver birches, some distance away, so he flew over to them.

He liked the look of their chalky white trunks, which he'd never tried out before. Without further delay, he began hammering on one.

While he was busy, Walter thought he heard a little giggle, so he stopped and listened for a moment. The giggling stopped, too, so Walter resumed his work. Then the giggling began again.

"Is someone laughing at me?" Walter wondered.

"Yes, it's me, the tree, but I'm not laughing at you, I'm giggling because you're tickling my trunk," the silver birch said.

"I'm sorry. I didn't mean to do that. I'll go away and find some other tree which isn't as ticklish," Walter replied.

"Oh, no, don't do that. I've never had such a beautiful feathered friend of my very own before. Stay and you can hammer on my trunk any time you want." The silver birch chuckled.

So Walter stayed and became good friends with the silver birches.

At last, he'd found a place where the trees accepted him for what he was and he could hammer away to his heart's content.

Isabella's New Umbrella

THERE was once a new umbrella that belonged to Isabella. She stood in the hall, in Isabella's house, next to a very old umbrella.

"When will Isabella take me out?" she asked him.

"Isabella will need you when it rains," he said.

"What's rain?" she asked. "I've never seen it."

"I'll try to explain this thing they call rain," he said. "It's lots of drops of water, in a cloud together. They come down from the sky — that is rainy weather."

"Will it rain soon?" the new umbrella asked.

"Soon enough," he said. He yawned and closed his eyes. "You'll have to work hard when it rains. Have a rest now — that's what I advise."

The new umbrella waited and waited.

"I'm tired of waiting," she said at last.

She opened the door and hopped into the garden. She whirled and twirled, and then unfurled, and stretched herself out in the sun.

"It's a sunshade!" Isabella's cat cried. He told all his friends. Soon countless cats were crammed in the shady spot under the umbrella. The purring was so loud all the birds had to fly next door to get some peace. A blackbird muttered something about calling the police.

The new umbrella was sorry she'd caused trouble.

"I'll go and wait until Isabella needs me," she said.

THE brand new umbrella, bought by Isabella, stood in the hall, in Isabella's house. She waited and waited.

"I'm tired of waiting," she said at last.

She opened the door and hopped down the road to the park. She whirled and twirled, and then unfurled, and stretched herself out on the grass.

Just then a breeze blew her on to the pond.

"Look! Look!" the ducks quacked. "It's a boat!"

"All aboard!" a duckling shouted. They all flopped into the umbrella and away they floated.

The gentle breeze blew them many miles all the way to Dungeness. The park keep took hours to find them — he got lost in Inverness.

The new umbrella was sor she'd caused trouble.

"I'll go and wait until Isabella needs me," she said.

48

THE brand-new umbrella, bought by Isabella, stood in the hall, in Isabella's house. She waited and waited.

"I'm tired of waiting," she said at last.

She opened the door and hopped all the way to town. She whirled and twirled, and then unfurled, and stretched herself out on the ground.

Just then a strong wind blew her up in the air.

"It's an aeroplane!" cried some dogs, who were waiting outside a shop. They hung on to the umbrella and away they blew.

They landed right on top of the town hall. A dachshund said he hoped they wouldn't fall.

"Fetch a parachute!" a big white dog, with lots of spots, cried. The mayor climbed up to rescue them and tore his civic suit.

The new umbrella went home. She was very sorry she'd caused trouble.

"It's no good," she said, with a sigh. "Isabella doesn't need me after all."

Suddenly, the old umbrella told her to look out of the window. Big drops of water were falling out of the sky.

"It's raining at last!" the new umbrella cried.

Just then Isabella came into the hall. She put on her coat, then she picked up the new umbrella and off they went.

The new umbrella stretched herself out as far as she could go. She felt so proud because she didn't let a single drop of rain fall on Isabella.

After that, she never minded waiting in the hall. She knew, whenever it rained, Isabella would need her.

49

Who Stole The Snowman's

THE night was cold and frosty, with the snow all crisp and deep,
When the Snowman closed his snowy eyes and then fell fast asleep.
But the Snowman was so very sad when he awoke next day,
For someone crept up in the night and took his hat away.

"And everyone said I looked so smart and it fitted me just right.
Who do you think would steal my hat when I slept in the night?
Would you ask and see if you can find who took my hat away?
I'd really like to have it back and then I'll smile all day."

Now the Snowman loved his special hat and tried hard not to cry,
But his friend the cheerful Robin saw the teardrops in his eye.
"You see, I've nothing else to wear," the Snowman sadly said,
"And I always felt so very proud with a hat upon my head.

So the Robin said he'd try his best and ask everyone he saw —
He plucked up lots of courage and asked the cat next door.
But the cat just said, "It wasn't me, for I don't need a hat,
And all last night, when the cold wind blew, I slept on the fireside mat."

50

Hat?

"It wasn't me,"
the rabbit said, "for I live
underground
And the hat would cover
my two ears and I wouldn't
hear a sound."
"And it wasn't me," said the
big black crow, "for I don't
mind the rain,
And if I'd taken it away, I'd
bring it back again."

Up in the sky the North
Wind blew and listened as
they spoke.
"I took the hat," he softly said,
"just for a little joke.
I didn't mean the Snowman
harm, I'm sorry if he's sad.
I did not know the hat he
wore was the only hat
he had."

And the North Wind now
felt so ashamed, while across
the land he blew,

So he found the hat, blew
off the dust, and it looked
just like new.
Then he blew it very
carefully, right on the
Snowman's head.
"You're the smartest
Snowman that I've seen,"
the North Wind
quietly said.

Well, the Snowman
was so happy that he
smiled the whole day
long
And the Robin sat
beside him and whistled a
special song.
And the rabbit and
the big black crow and
even next door's cat,
Were very pleased
and happy that
the Snowman had
his hat!

Alice Has Fun!

THIS would be a nice day to go to the beach. Will you take me?" Alice said to Mummy one hot, summer day.

"I'm sorry," Mummy replied. "I have to stay at home. I'm expecting a man to come and mend the washing machine. You'll have to play in the garden today."

Frisky, Mrs Green's cat, from next door, jumped over the wall into Alice's garden. Alice played chase the ball with him, but soon Frisky felt too hot and went into a shady place under a bush where he fell asleep.

Then Alice rode her hobby horse round the lawn, but it was too hot for galloping along, so she put it back in the shed.

It would be nice to paddle and splash in the cold waves today, she thought, and she wished she was at the beach.

Just then Mummy came out into the garden.

"Dear me," she said, "I didn't know it was so hot out here. Alice, come in and get your sun hat."

"I expect it's in my room," Alice said and she ran upstairs to look.

SHE looked in the drawers where her T-shirts and shorts were kept, but she couldn't find her sun hat.

She looked in her sock drawer and the wardrobe where her dresses were hanging, but she didn't find her sun hat. And it wasn't on her coat pegs nor on her bookshelves.

Maybe I've put it in my toy cupboard, she thought, and started to look in there. What a lot of interesting things she found. There was a sand pail shaped like a castle.

"I don't know what I'll do with this in the garden," she said to herself, "but I'll take it out anyway."

Further in the cupboard was a little jug and she put it into the pail.

NEXT, she took out a box and emptied it out on the floor. Among all sorts of things, she spotted a fish and a turtle she used to play with in the bath when she was a baby.

"I'd forgotten all about you," she said, and she popped the fish and turtle into her pail.

There was a green velvet bag full of shells. She put that in the pail, too.

Alice stood on tip-toe and looked on the top shelf of the cupboard. There stood a dolls' cradle. In it was a tiny doll and on top of the tiny doll, all folded up to be a blanket, was Alice's sun hat. Alice laid the doll in her pail, picked it and her sun hat up, and ran downstairs.

"I've found my sun hat, Mummy."

Mummy looked at the pailful of toys.

"What a mixture of toys you've got there," she said. "What are you going to do with so many?"

"I don't know," Alice replied. "Can you think of something I could do with them?"

"Well, let me think," Mummy said. "Let's see what you've got."

She looked through Alice's pailful, and then she smiled.

"We'll fill the paddling pool," she suggested. "Then I think you'll be able to play with all of them."

Soon, Alice had decorated the grass round the paddling pool with shells. She floated her fish and turtle in the water,

and taught the tiny doll to swim.

After that she had great fun filling her jug and pouring water into the pail.

"I'm pretending I'm at the beach," she told Mummy at lunchtime.

"What a clever girl you are, to make your very own beach," Mummy said.

53

WOO'S GOOD IDEA

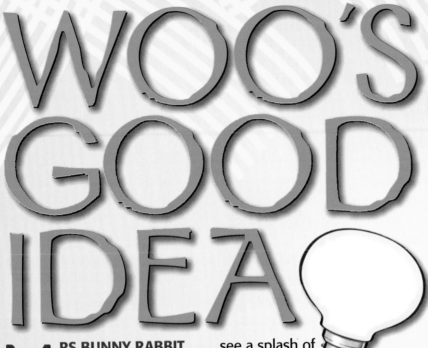

MRS BUNNY RABBIT was hurrying through the forest, followed by her twins, Bessie and Bobby.

Although the sun was shining, it was a cold day, and Mrs Rabbit was afraid that her children would catch a chill. They would keep stopping to pick wild flowers to take home to their grandmother.

"Oh, do hurry, children," Mrs Rabbit said. "You'll catch cold and be ill."

"Can we pick just a few more flowers, Mummy, please?" Bessie asked. "We've only got a little bunch."

"Well, be as quick as you can," Mrs Rabbit replied. "I'm nearly frozen. I want to get home to the fire and our nice hot supper."

"Oh, look," Bobby said. "There must be some flowers over by that elm tree. I can

see a splash of yellow and a splash of red. Let's go and see."

They all went over to investigate, but it wasn't flowers at all. It was two large balls of wool, one yellow and one red.

"How strange," Mrs Bunny Rabbit said. "I wonder who could have left two balls of wool in the forest?

"I think we should take them to the Police Station so that Constable Plod can find out who owns them."

SO off they went to the Police Station. Constable Plod opened up his big report book and searched the pages.

"Ah, yes," he said. "Mrs Piggy Twiggy reported that she lost two balls of wool in the forest, but she doesn't want them back as she has finished her knitting.

"She said that whoever finds them can keep them. You can take them away again, Mrs Rabbit."

Mrs Bunny Rabbit was pleased. She decided to use the wool to knit nice warm scarves and hats for the twins. One twin could have a yellow set and the other could have a red set.

But the twins argued about who should have which colour.

"I'd like the yellow one," Bessie said.

"No, I'd like the yellow one," Bobby said.

"You can't both have the yellow one," Mrs Bunny Rabbit said. "One of you will have to have red."

"But I don't like red very much," Bessie said.

"And I don't like red, either," Bobby said.

"What tiresome, ungrateful children you are," their mother said. "I've a good mind to give the wool to Mrs Henny Jenny for her chicks and let you go without.

"But it's cold in our burrow and I don't want you catching frost-bite. We'll ask Woo, the wise old owl, to settle this dispute for us."

So off they went to find Woo. They found him huddled up at the foot of the oak tree, snuggling into his feathers to keep warm.

"Hello," he said. "Isn't it cold? My feathers don't keep the wind out like they used to. You look worried, Mrs Rabbit. Can I help you?"

Mrs Bunny Rabbit explained that Bessie and Bobby were arguing about who should have the red scarf and hat and who should have the yellow.

"It's a real problem, Woo. Can you tell me what to do?" she asked.

WOO closed his eyes and looked serious.

"I'll think of a solution," he said.

He spent such a long time sitting there with his eyes closed that Mrs Bunny Rabbit thought he had gone to sleep.

But, after a while, he opened his eyes.

"Of course," he said. "There is only one answer.

"You must knit the scarves and hats in stripes of red and yellow, then they will be exactly the same. The twins can have identical sets and everybody will be happy."

"What a wonderful idea, Woo!" Mrs Rabbit clapped in delight. "Does that suit you, twins?"

"Suits me.

I quite like stripes," Bessie said.

"I quite like stripes, too," Bobby said.

So Mrs Bunny Rabbit knitted two beautiful striped scarves and two little striped hats for the twins. And she was so grateful to Woo for his good advice that she knitted him a striped scarf and a striped hat with the left-over wool.

That meant that from then on Woo was able to keep warm even in the coldest weather, just like Bessie and Bobby.

55

The Cow Who Lost Her Moo

IT was a pouring-with-rain day. Carlotta the Cow pranced round the field, splashing through the long grass.

"I'm having such fun — moo, moo! Jumping like a kangaroo!" she said.

"You'll catch cold," the other cows said. "Come and shelter under the tree with us."

Carlotta didn't take any notice. She paddled in puddles, and balanced raindrops on her nose. Soon she was so wet that water even tickle-trickled from her tail.

"I'm having such fun — moo, moo! Jumping like a . . . A-TISH-OO!"

"You stood in wet grass up to your knees," said the other cows. "We're not surprised you've started to sneeze."

Carlotta opened her mouth, but not a sound came out.

She had lost her moo. She went to the pigsty, to see if Priscilla the Pig could help. Priscilla was asleep, her piglets by her side.

Carlotta sniffed — she rolled her eyes, too, but all she could say was, "A-TISH-OO!"

"I can tell at a glance you've lost your moo," said Priscilla, "so I'll give a few of my grunts to you."

"Grunt," said Carlotta. It didn't sound quite right for a cow, but she grunted thank you anyhow.

The piglets thought Carlotta was another pig. They followed her to the field and played hide-and-seek among the cows' legs.

"We really wish they weren't here," said the cows, with a sigh. Carlotta had to lead the piglets back to their sty.

Then she went to the stable, to see if Hamlet the Horse could help. Hamlet was eating some hay. A foal stood close by.

Carlotta sniffed — she rolled her eyes, too, but all she could say was, "A-TISH-OO!"

"I can tell at a glance you've lost your moo," said Hamlet, "so I'll give a few of my neighs to you."

"Neigh," said Carlotta. It didn't sound quite right for a cow, but she neighed a thank you anyhow.

THE foal thought Carlotta was another horse. He followed her to the field and lolloped about, tripping up all the cows.

"We wish he'd go. He can't stand still. He's just not able," said the cows. Carlotta had to take the foal back to his stable.

56

Then she went to the next field, to see if Shawn the Sheep could help. Shawn was playing follow-my-leader with seventeen sheep.

Carlotta sniffed — she rolled her eyes, too, but all she could say was, "A-TISH-OO!"

"I can see at a glance you've lost your moo," said Shawn, "so I'll give a few of my baas to you."

"Baa," said Carlotta. It didn't sound quite right for a cow, but she baa'd a thank you, anyhow.

THE seventeen sheep thought she was one of the flock. They followed her to the field and began to graze.

"Look! They're eating our grass!" said the cows, with a shout. Farmer Brown came to see what the fuss was about.

When he saw how wet Carlotta was, he took her to the cosy cowshed.

I'll never find my moo,

she thought sadly. But, before you could say "bread and milk", she dried out and warmed up.

And the very next time she opened her mouth, she didn't say, "A-TISH-OO!" she said, "MOO."

"You'll shelter with us next time, won't you," said the other cows, but Carlotta only said, "Moo, moo."

ACTIVITY

CAN YOU MOO LIKE A COW?

What other animal noises can you make?

The Scarecrow's Picnic

ONCE there were three scarecrows. Whitie stood in Farmer White's field, Blackie scared the crows off Farmer Black's field, and Greenie looked after a field belonging to Farmer Green.

The three were good friends, and when the moon was a pale pearl in the night sky, and people were in bed, they visited one another.

One sunny autumn day, some grown-ups and children arrived in the field next to Whitie's one. They played games with balls, a whistle blew and they ran races. And when everybody sat down on the grass to have their tea, there was merry music.

Whitie watched everything with great interest.

"What's going on next door?" Whitie asked Robin Redbreast who'd perched on his shoulder.

"The people say they're having a picnic."

"So that's what it is — a picnic," said Whitie. "It looks great fun. I'll have one, too. Robin, would you please go and invite Blackie and Greenie to come to a picnic when the moon begins to shine tonight?"

"Certainly." Off Robin flew.

WHITIE'S next visitor was Rosie Rabbit. She, too, had watched the people's picnic so, when she heard Whitie say he was going to have one, she lolloped up to him.

"Whitie, you'll need a ball for your picnic," she told him.

"Where will I find a ball?" Whitie wondered.

"I know where Farmer White threw away some turnips his sheep didn't want," said Rosie. "The turnips are round like balls. I'll go and fetch one."

Next, up popped Mandy Mouse out of Whitie's waistcoat pocket.

"Whitie," she squeaked, "I was at the people's picnic, and there were delicious cakes and biscuits to nibble. You must have nice food at your picnic."

"Whatever can we have?" Whitie looked worried.

"Don't worry, I can gather berries and mushrooms in the wood for you," Mandy said.

Mandy had just left Whitie when Stevie Starling landed on one of his arms.

ACTIVITY

LOOK AND SEE IF YOU CAN SPOT MANDY MOUSE.

58

"Robin told me you're having a picnic tonight. Can I help?" Stevie asked.

"Mmm, let me think for a minute," said Whitie.

"Yes — I know what else we need — a whistle to start the races and music while we eat."

"You've come to the right bird." Stevie puffed out his chest. "I can whistle and I can sing so I'll start the races and make music while you eat."

"Thank you, Stevie. That's everything we need for a picnic," said Whitie happily.

THAT night the picnic field was bathed in moonlight. Whitie and his helpers got everything ready.

Then, along the road stumped Blackie and Greenie Scarecrow.

"What's a picnic?" they asked.

"We'll show you, for we saw one in this very field today," said Rosie Rabbit, and she rolled the turnip ball to Blackie's feet. "Let's start with ball games."

SO Whitie showed them how to play football as he'd seen the people do.

After that, Stevie Starling made the three scarecrows stand in a line, and whistled to start the races. They ran, hopped, jumped and crawled.

"Now," said Whitie, "we'll all sit down on the grass and have our picnic tea."

They sat down, and Mandy Mouse shared out berries and mushrooms, and Stevie sang songs while they ate.

The sky began to lighten and the moon to fade away.

"Thank you, everybody, for a lovely picnic," said Blackie.

"Yes, thank you," said Greenie. "Picnics are going to be one of my favourite things from now on."

"And now we must go for we have to start work when the sun peeps over the hill," said Blackie.

"Goodbye," called everyone as the two happy scarecrows stumped down the road to their fields.

59

GRANDAD'S BIRTHDAY

"IT will be Grandad's birthday soon," Mummy said. "I know you all said you were going to make something for him this year, instead of buying him a present. How are you getting on?"

"I've made him a set of wooden book-ends at school," Fraser said. "I only have to varnish them now and they'll be finished."

"I've knitted him a pair of nice warm gloves," Eleanor said. "I love knitting, and I know Grandad's hands get cold in the winter."

"And what have you made, Claire?" Mummy asked. "I hope you have managed to make something."

Poor little Claire looked very crestfallen.

"I haven't got anything made yet," she confessed. "I was trying to knit a scarf to match Eleanor's gloves but

60

I dropped so many of the stitches that the knitting was full of holes. I'm no good at doing things."

"But don't forget Fraser is ten years old and Eleanor is eight," Mummy reminded her. "You are still only six and have a lot to learn. Anyway, I know something that you are very good at. You are good at helping me in the kitchen."

"But how will that help me to make something for Grandad's birthday?" Claire asked. "I can't go and do his cooking for him, even if I could cook."

"If you wait until this afternoon I'll show you what you can do."

AFTER lunch Fraser and Eleanor went off to play with their friends and Mummy and Claire went into the kitchen to begin Claire's cooking lesson.

"What I think you could do, Claire," Mummy said, "is make some fairy cakes for Grandad. You have helped me to make them many times, and if I tell you what to do you can do the actual work. That could be your home-made gift."

Claire thought this was a wonderful idea. She loved helping Mummy in the kitchen, and felt sure she could make the cakes with just a little help from Mummy.

"I'll begin by weighing out the ingredients," Claire said. "I know everything has to be just right."

Watched by Mummy, Claire weighed the flour, fat and sugar and made sure the eggs were well beaten. Then she creamed the fat and sugar together until the mixture was soft and fluffy.

"Do I add the eggs now?" she asked.

"That's right," Mummy told her. "Then blend in the flour through the sieve so that no lumps get through."

When everything was done to Mummy's satisfaction Claire put the mixture into the paper cases and Mummy put them into the oven to cook.

"Doesn't the kitchen smell nice, Mummy?"

"Yes, that's one of the things I love about baking day," Mummy replied.

When the cakes were ready Mummy took them out of the oven and put them on a wire tray to cool. When they were cold she showed Claire how to make lemon icing and let Claire do the icing herself.

"I think they would look nice with some decorations on top," Claire decided. "I'll put cherry halves on some,

and maybe a few chocolate drops, too."

WHEN Fraser and Eleanor came back home they saw the nice cakes and told Claire she was very clever and they would love a cake to taste!

"Don't worry." Claire smiled. "I've made extra so we can all have one for tea."

The cakes tasted delicious, and when Grandad got his birthday presents he was delighted.

"What clever grandchildren I have," he said. "Not many people get such lovely home-made gifts."

And now Claire makes fairy cakes for every family birthday.

She has found something she's good at.

ACTIVITY

LOOK AT THE MAIN PICTURE.

Can you see two ingredients that you need to make cakes?

61

A seal pup called Blue

THE seal pup called Blue loved to swim in the sea. He rolled over the waves and dived very deep, and chased silver-tailed fish to have for his tea.

When the tide was low, the grown-up seals slipped ashore. Blue swam alone, but it wasn't fun any more.

"Mummy," he called. "Will you swim with me?"

"Not now, dear one," she replied. "I'm basking in the sun."

"Daddy," Blue called. "Will you swim in the sea with me?"

"Not now, dear son," Daddy replied. "I'm guarding everyone." The other seals were all fast asleep.

"I'll find someone on the shore," said Blue.

"Whizzo!" shouted a seagull overhead. "I'll help you explore."

"Be back when the sun slides down the sky," Mummy Seal said. "We'll all swim south when the tide is high."

Blue set off. Soon, he came to a rock pool. He stared into the water. In the pool, Blue saw a seal pup, just like himself.

"Will you swim in the sea with me?" he asked, clapping his flippers excitedly.

The other seal clapped, too. Blue swam right round the pool, but he couldn't find the seal anywhere.

The seagull swooped down and whispered in Blue's small ear.

"You've made a mistake, all young animals do. That wasn't a seal, but a reflection of you!"

Blue was disappointed.

"I'll have to look elsewhere, then," he said.

"Wacko!" shouted the seagull. "Try and try again!"

Before long, Blue came to a cave in the Cliffside.

"Is anyone there?" he called. "I'm a seal pup."

Straight away, Blue heard a sound.

". . . Seal pup . . . seal pup . . . pup."

"There must be a seal pup in there!" he cried.

"Will you swim in the sea with me?" he asked, clapping his flippers excitedly.

Blue heard the other seal clapping, too. He looked in the cave, but he couldn't find the seal anywhere.

The seagull swooped down and whispered in Blue's small ear.

"You've made a mistake, all young animals do. That wasn't a seal, but an echo of you."

Blue was disappointed.

"I'll look further round the bay," he said, after a while.

"Right-o," cried the gull. "Look harder, I say."

JUST then, the sun shone into the cave. Up on the wall, Blue saw a seal pup just like himself, only black and bigger.

"Will you swim in the sea with me?" he asked, clapping his flippers excitedly.

Blue saw the other seal clapping, too. He went right up to the wall, but he couldn't find the seal anywhere.

62

The seagull swooped down and whispered in Blue's ear.

"You've made a mistake, all young animals do. That wasn't a seal, but a shadow of you."

"I'll have to swim all alone," said Blue. Sadly, he went back to the edge of the sea. Then he had a surprise.

"Bingo!" shouted the seagull.

"Come and meet your new brother," Mummy Seal said.

"Oh, no, I'm not going to make another mistake," said Blue. "That's not a real seal pup."

But this time it was.

"Will you swim in the sea with me?" asked Blue.

"Of course I will," his brother replied.

They had such fun. They rolled over the waves and dived very deep and chased silver-tailed fish to have for their tea.

"Now, I'll always have someone to swim with me," Blue said happily.

63

M ISS TWEEDY
ran the laundry
In her little country
town.
But one day she
discovered
Her machine had
broken down!

"What shall I do?"
she cried, aghast.
"Without a good
machine
There is no way that
I'll get
People's washing really
clean!"

"No towels, no sheets,
no tablecloths,
No vests, no smart
white shirts,
No uniforms for school,
no socks,
No trousers, and
no skirts!"

Her next-door
neighbour heard her
cries
And said, "Stop
crying, do.
I think it's very likely
I can be of help
to you."

VROOM!

"I'm working on a
new idea,"
The old inventor said.
"I'll go and fetch it
straight away —
It's in my garden shed."

He came back soon, and
brought what was
A shock to everyone.
"My robot friend will
help," he said,
"To get your washing
done."

With that, the robot
whirred and buzzed.
His wheels began
to spin.
Miss Tweedy scratched
her head, and said,
"You'd better both
come in."

She showed the robot
all the clothes
Still waiting to be done,
Then sat down on a
kitchen chair
And cried, "This should
be fun!"

"I never get to just
relax —
There's always lots
to do.
But now I can enjoy
myself
And leave the work
to you!"

The robot placed the
washing in
His great big metal
tummy,
Then swung around,
and back and
forth —
He really did look
funny!

But when he'd done,
Miss Tweedy smiled.
"Well, I declare!"
she cried.
The clothes were now
not only clean
But even
tumble-dried!

From that day on,
Miss Tweedy
Has lots of time to spare.
For, thanks to her
inventor friend,
She doesn't have
a care!

The Metal Man

NO ROOM FOR PONGO

PONGO was just a puppy when he came to live at Blueberry Farm.

"Now don't go fussing over him," Farmer Ted told Michael and Sally. "He's a farm dog, not a pet."

But everyone did fuss over Pongo. Mrs Ted gave him little treats to eat, and when she went shopping, she bought him a ball. Michael and Sally played with Pongo and gave him lots of hugs. The puppy followed them everywhere.

Pongo was a good little dog. He didn't dig up the garden or chase the hens. He learned how to help Farmer Ted with the sheep and cows and, if a fox came slinking about, Pongo barked a warning.

After a long day working on the farm, Farmer Ted liked to relax before the fire in his favourite chair. He'd put his feet up and read the newspaper.

One evening he found Pongo curled up in his chair. Farmer Ted laughed.

"This is my chair, Pongo. There's no room for you," he said.

Mrs Ted had a rocking-chair. After her busy day was over, she would sit down, sighing happily as she picked up her knitting. Sometimes she just sat quietly, gently rocking backwards and forwards, thinking happy thoughts.

One evening she found Pongo in her chair. Mrs Ted smiled. Pongo looked so comfortable, his little nose twitching as he dreamed doggy dreams.

Mrs Ted gave him a little shake.

"Wake up, Pongo," she said. "There's no room for both of us."

Michael's chair was soft and bouncy with lots of cushions. Sometimes, he pretended his chair was a spaceship bound for Mars — or a submarine exploring the ocean.

ONE evening he found Pongo curled up in the chair, his nose twitching as he dreamed doggy dreams.

"Look at Pongo," he shouted. "He thinks this is his chair. I'm sorry, boy, there's no room for you."

Sally's chair was soft and pretty. When she snuggled down among the cushions, she felt like a princess. There was room in the chair for Sally and her family of dolls and Teddy bears. But there was no room for Pongo.

There he was, curled up in Sally's chair one evening, his nose twitching as he dreamed doggy dreams.

"You're squashing Mr Ted and Baby Betty," Sally said. "I'm sorry, Pongo. There's no room for you."

Poor Pongo — he lay on his mat with his head resting on his paws.

How sad he looked.

IT'S not fair," Michael said. "Why can't Pongo have a chair?"

"Because Pongo is a farm dog," Farmer Ted told him.

"But everyone else has a chair," Sally said. "Pongo should have a chair, too."

Mrs Ted nodded as she rocked backwards and forwards.

"Pongo is a good dog and he works very hard," she said. "I wonder — there's that old chair in the barn. I could make a new cover . . ."

"And Pongo can have one of my cushions," Michael said.

"And one of mine," Sally said. "Please, Daddy . . ."

When Farmer Ted said it would be all right, Michael and Sally could hardly wait for morning to get started.

First, they shooed the hens out of the old chair and brushed away the cobwebs and dust. Then Mrs Ted found an old curtain and made a smart new cover for the chair.

That evening Farmer Ted sat with his feet up, reading his newspaper.

Mrs Ted sighed happily as she rocked and thought her happy thoughts.

Michael pretended his chair was a magic carpet, zooming over mountains and rooftops to distant lands. Sally cuddled Baby Betty and sang her a lullaby.

And Pongo — he was curled up in front of the fire in his own special chair. Pongo's nose twitched as he dreamed his doggy dreams. Pongo's chair was deep and wide, the cushions soft — plenty of room for a sleepy little farm dog.

GRAMPA

THE animals and birds of Lapwater Lake were all feeling very excited. Soon they would be holding their yearly talent show on the lake. It was always a great occasion.

Grampa Swan was also looking forward to the special day, but not as much as usual.

"I'm too old to enter the competition any more." He sighed to himself.

"Still, it will be fun to watch the youngsters enjoying themselves."

What Grampa Swan didn't realise was that some of the young animals were a bit worried about the contest.

"I'm entering the lily pad leap-frog event for the first time ever," little Fiona Frog told her friend, Debbie Duck. "I've been practising my leaps for days, but they're not very good."

Debbie Duck had a suggestion.

"You could ask Grampa Swan for help," she said. "He doesn't leap or jump himself, but he's been to lots of shows over the years. He might be able to help."

Fiona Frog thought that was a brilliant idea. She visited Grampa Swan at once.

"I may not be a frog," he said happily, "but I've seen lots of frog leaping events and know all the best moves. I'll soon have you leaping well."

BY the time Fiona Frog had had a few lessons with Grampa Swan, she was much more confident and excited about the big day.

"There's nothing that Grampa Swan doesn't know about the talent show," she

SWAN

told Donny Duck happily.

"Do you think he might have time to help me, too?" Donny Duck asked hopefully. "I don't know what to do about my swimming display — it's terrible."

Fiona Frog laughed kindly.

"I think you're another pupil for Grampa Swan," she declared.

Grampa Swan was delighted to see Donny Duck.

"By the time I've finished with you, you'll have the best swimming display ever," he told him.

Word soon got around. If any of the young animals or birds had any problems over their performance, Grampa Swan was the one to see.

He found time to help Kelly Kingfisher with her deep water dives, and even gave Wilfred Warbler some singing lessons.

"I can't sing a tune myself," Grampa Swan confessed, "but I do know a good tune when I hear one — and I know what the judges like!"

AT last the day of Lapwater Lake's Talent Show arrived. As

Grampa Swan wasn't entering the competition, he stood by the side of the lake and watched.

Soon the events were in full swing. Grampa Swan's pupils all did very well. When Fiona Frog came first in the lily pad leap-frog he clapped the loudest of all.

Both Donny Duck and Wilfred Warbler won prizes, too.

"I'd never have made top place without Grampa Swan's help," Fiona Frog told the judges as she received her winner's trophy.

"We wouldn't have won prizes without his help, either," Donny Duck and Wilfred Warbler chorused. "Grampa Swan coached us brilliantly."

Kelly Kingfisher was happy, too.

"My dive didn't win, but it's still the best I've ever done," she said proudly. "I think Grampa Swan deserves a medal for all his help!"

The judges agreed — and they had another surprise, too.

"Grampa Swan, we're presenting you with a medal for best coach. And we'd like you to do a lap of honour around the lake."

Grampa Swan was so surprised that he almost lost his balance and fell into the water. He proudly swam three laps around Lapwater Lake as everyone cheered and clapped.

Grampa Swan thought it was the best contest he had ever known!

69

it's magic

ALL day long, Chloe Caterpillar crawled round the garden, eating leaves. "I'm terribly bored," she said. "Nothing happens to me."

"Keep on eating your leaves, and just wait and see," said all the other caterpillars.

She crawled to the pond and saw some tadpoles squiggling about in the water. They looked like little black dots, with long tails.

She crawled round the bushes and saw a bird in its nest. It was sitting quietly on four speckly blue eggs.

She crawled along the

flower beds and saw lots of buds on fresh green stems.

"I'm terribly bored," she said. "Nothing happens to me."

"Keep on eating your leaves, and just wait and see," said all the other caterpillars.

DAY after day she nibbled the leaves. She grew bigger and stronger.

One day, Chloe Caterpillar went to the pond again. The tadpoles were much bigger. Now they had legs, and their tails had disappeared. They had turned into frogs.

"It's magic!" she cried.

The frogs hopped about on the grass, jumping over each other.

Chloe Caterpillar crawled away, with a sigh.

She looked at the speckly eggs in the nest. Suddenly the shells cracked open. Out popped some baby birds.

"It's magic!" she cried.

The birds twittered and opened their beaks as wide as they could.

"We're going to fly, gliding and soaring high in the sky," they said.

Chloe Caterpillar crawled away, with a sigh.

She went to look at the buds in the flower beds. Slowly their petals unfolded in the sun. The buds turned into beautiful flowers.

"It's magic!" she cried.

The flowers swayed and danced in the breeze.

"We're glad we're in bloom, giving such pleasure to everyone," they said.

Chloe Caterpillar sighed.

"Nothing happens to me," she said.

"Now you just wait and see," said the other caterpillars.

ONE day, Chloe Caterpillar just couldn't keep still.

"My skin feels too tight," she said. "There's something not right."

The other caterpillars couldn't keep still either.

"There's no need to worry about all of this," they said. "It's because you're becoming a chrysalis."

"I say, what a thrill!

Something's happening to me!" said Chloe Caterpillar.

"We need a rest now, let's just hang on a tree," said the other caterpillars.

When Chloe Caterpillar woke up she str-etched, and she str-etched. Then she had a surprise. While she'd been asleep she had grown wings.

"It's magic!" she cried. "It's really happened to me!"

"You're a butterfly now," said the other caterpillars. "And so are we."

Chloe Caterpillar opened and closed her wings in the sunshine, admiring their lovely colours.

Then she flew happily away, high over the garden, with all the other new butterflies.

LET'S have an Autumn Afternoon," Mummy said one bright, sunny October day. "We'll ask Grandma and Grandpa to come and join us in the garden."

"What happens on an Autumn Afternoon?" Peter and Patricia wanted to know.

"We'll do things we can only do in autumn," Mummy explained.

AUTUMN LEAVES

But when Mummy phoned Grandma and Grandpa she discovered that Grandma had twisted her ankle, and the doctor wanted her to sit with her foot up on a footstool.

"It would have been lovely to come for an Autumn Afternoon," Grandma said. "I'm so sorry I can't come, but Grandpa will walk over. Don't worry about me. I have a new book to read."

THEY went out into the garden.

"First we must sweep up the leaves that have fallen from the trees," Mummy said. "But save some of the prettiest, for I know something we could do with them."

Grandpa arrived as Peter was raking leaves off the grass, and Mummy and Patricia were sweeping them into piles on the paths. Grandpa fetched the wheelbarrow and wheeled the leaves to a special box at the bottom of the garden.

Each time, he gave Peter and Patricia rides in the barrow. It was great fun.

When the leaves had been tidied into the special box, and Mummy had put a few pretty ones indoors, Peter asked what they would do next.

"Well," Mummy said, "the apples are ripe on the apple tree. Would you like to pick them?"

"Ooh, yes," the children cried.

Mummy found a basket for the apples, and Grandpa brought the ladder out of the garage so that he could climb up the high branches.

By and by, the basket was full of apples, and they took it into the kitchen.

"Now, put on your painting aprons," Mummy said, "and I'll show you how to make an autumn picture for Grandma."

Mummy painted the bumpy side of one of the leaves they'd kept bright yellow. Then she pressed the leaf on a sheet of paper. When she lifted it, there was the print of a pretty yellow leaf.

"It's lovely," Patricia said.

"You can make prints of all the leaves you've saved," Mummy said, "in red, orange, green and brown as well as yellow."

While the children were busy printing leaves, Grandpa peeled apples and Mummy made pastry.

"I'm going to make two apple pies," she explained. "One for Daddy to have when he comes home for tea, and one for Grandma."

When the pies were cooked, they all drove to Grandma's with the leafy picture and an apple pie.

"Did you have a nice Autumn Afternoon?" Grandma asked.

"Yes," they said and they told Grandma all about it.

"What did you do, Grandma?" Peter asked.

"I'm still doing it. Come quietly and see," Grandma said softly.

THE children tip-toed to Grandma's chair by the window. On the lawn were two red squirrels.

"They're making their autumn store of nuts before winter comes," Grandma whispered.

"Now, look up at the telephone wire."

Along the wire sat a row of birds with long tails.

"Those birds are swallows and, seeing it's autumn, they're getting ready to fly to Africa away from our cold winter," Grandma explained. "So, you see, I've been having an Autumn Afternoon as well."

They watched the squirrels and the swallows for a little while, and then Mummy gave them all a slice of apple pie with cream poured over it. It was delicious.

"What a nice way to end an Autumn Afternoon," Grandpa said, and the others thought so, too.

73

King Grumble

KING GRUMBLEGRUMPS had lost his crown.
Was in an awful state.
He'd looked all up, he'd looked all down!
He cried, "I shall be late!"

Queen said, "Well, you should put your things
Back in their proper place."
But she felt sorry for the king
When she saw his sad face.

"I'm opening that new swimming pool,"
King said. "I'll miss the fun."
The queen said, "I will ring the school —
You'll have to miss this one!"

The queen got out her sewing kits,
The royal rag-bag, too.
She found a lot of useful bits
As good wives always do.

She made the king a lovely crown
And put it on his head.
But Grumbles grumbled, with a frown.
"No! This won't do," he said.

"For it must have some jewels, too —
It looks so very plain."
The queen said, "There's no pleasing you!"
And took it off again.

So, then she found some pretty beads,
All purple, blue and red.
The king said, "Just what this crown needs,"
And clapped it on his head.

Then off they went. The sky was blue —
It was a lovely day.
The king received a loud "Thank you,"
The queen a big bouquet.

But, suddenly, the king slipped down
And in the pool he fell

And, naturally, his makeshift crown
Went in with him, as well!

The children swam to lend a hand.
It made them very happy —
It wasn't planned, but they felt grand —
To help this kingly chappie!

At last King Grumbles scrambled out —
Dry clothes for him were found.
The king and queen went walkabout
To see things all around.

When they got home, they searched again —
They looked down low, up high,
But, sadly, all in vain.
A tear came to King's eye.

Then, picking up his dressing-gown,
He saw, with glad surprise,
Beneath its folds, the missing crown
Shone before his eyes!

grumps Loses
His Crown

The Terrible Twins

PROFESSOR WILLY-NILLY was looking after his four-year-old grandsons, Hugh and Fred.

As the twins were exactly alike, the only way anyone could tell them apart was for Hugh to be dressed in blue and Fred to be dressed in red.

This was the Professor's idea and everyone agreed that it worked very well.

The Professor loved looking after the twins as they always had such fun together and they liked him to join in their games.

He asked them what they wanted to do.

"Could we have the tin bath out and sail our boats, Grandpa?" Hugh, who loved playing with water, asked.

"I don't see why not," the Professor replied. "But you mustn't get your clothes wet or your mother will be cross."

"We'll be careful, Grandpa," Fred, who also loved playing with water, said.

So they played at sailing their boats and Professor Willy-Nilly got down on his knees and joined them.

They soon had a whole fleet of little ships bobbing about in the tin bath, transporting small stones and little bits of wood from one side of the bath to the other.

AFTER a while Hugh asked his grandpa if they could paddle.

"I don't see why not," the Professor replied. "But you mustn't get your clothes wet or your mother will be cross."

"We'll be careful, Grandpa," Hugh promised.

So Hugh took off his blue socks and his blue jumper and Fred took off his red socks and his red jumper and

they stepped into the water and splashed their feet about to make waves.

It looked such a lot of fun that the Professor decided to join them. He took off his socks, rolled up his trouser legs and stepped into the water.

His feet were so big that the water overflowed, making a big puddle on the lawn.

"Never mind," he said. "It'll save me watering the lawn."

They had such a pleasant time that the afternoon passed quickly. Then it was nearly time for the twins' mother to come to take them home.

"Come on, twins," the Professor said. "Let's get you dressed before your mother comes back."

He dried their feet and started to dress them, but without their socks and jumpers on, he didn't know which twin was which.

He put the blue socks and the blue jumper on Fred and the red socks and the red jumper on Hugh.

The twins didn't tell the Professor that he had made a mistake.

When their mother called for them, she asked if they'd had a good time.

"Super, Mummy," Hugh, who was wearing Fred's red clothes, said.

"Yes, super, Mummy," Fred, who was wearing Hugh's blue clothes, said.

"Say thank you to Grandpa and then we must get home. It's time you two had supper and went to bed."

So the twins thanked the Professor for looking after them and said how much they'd enjoyed paddling and playing with their boats.

"Come again soon, Fred," the Professor said, giving Hugh a hug.

"Come again soon, Hugh," the Professor said, giving Fred a hug.

"We will, Grandpa," the twins said together, then they burst out laughing. And they laughed and laughed all the way home.

"I wonder why the twins are laughing so much?" the Professor said. "I must have said something funny."

Hugh and Fred didn't tell their mother about the trick they had played till she was tucking them up in their beds. Then she laughed, too.

ACTIVITY

WHICH TWIN IS FRED AND WHICH IS HUGH?

Are you quite sure?

77

Rufus Stickleback

RUFUS STICKLEBACK was a wee red dragon who lived at the castle of King Horace and Queen Dolina.

Rufus was not very happy. Firstly, it was raining hard and, secondly, he had nothing to do. Having nothing to do in good weather wasn't nearly as bad as having nothing to do in the wet.

Rufus had tried hard to find something to do. Everybody else in the castle had something to do, except him.

"I'll help you to chase the mice from the pantry," he said to Tibby, the kitchen cat.

"No," Tibby sniffed. "I deal with the mice."

"Can I help with the cooking?" Rufus asked the cook and the kitchen maids.

"No, thank you, Rufus," they all chorused, "we'll manage."

"I'll help you to guard the castle," Rufus said to Ranald and Torquil, the two big dogs that guarded the castle gate.

"No, no," they replied, shaking their big grey heads. "We couldn't have that. You might let anybody in."

"Is there anything I can do in here?" Rufus asked the chancellor who sat in an office full of papers and leather-bound books.

"Can you do accounts?" the chancellor asked.

"Well . . . no," Rufus replied.

"In that case, there isn't anything you can help with here," said the chancellor, shaking his head. All the clerks looked up from the ledgers and shook their heads in agreement.

So it went on. Rufus trailed round the stables, the dairy, the garden and the farm in search of a job, but he could find none.

Rufus was still trying to think of something to do when he noticed that there seemed to be some kind of commotion going on.

Everybody in the castle was heading for the kitchen.

HE soon discovered what the cause of all the fuss was. With all the rain there wasn't a dry stick of firewood to be had in the kingdom. The castle fire had gone out and nobody could get it going again.

The cook and the queen were huffing and puffing at the fire with bellows but to no avail.

The knights were arguing among themselves about where to go on a quest to get some good coals.

The chancellor was trying to light the fire with some of his documents. It was as bad as that!

The court poet was making up a lament, but, above all, in a very loud voice, the king was demanding his tea.

Rufus had an idea. He wiggled his way to the front of the crowd, took a deep breath and blew flames at the fire with all his might.

Under such a blast of heat the coals soon caught and the kettle began to boil for the king's tea.

EVERYBODY was very excited and congratulated Rufus on his quick thinking.

"Well done, Rufus Stickleback!" cried the king. "From now on you are the official fire lighter for the castle."

Rufus was very pleased and so was everybody else.

"No more fiddling with bellows!" the cook sang.

"No more smouldering bonfires!" cheered the gardener.

"Hot tea!" chirped the king and queen.

From that day on, Rufus Stickleback was one of the happiest and busiest dragons in the kingdom.

79

The Runaway Aeroplane

CHAMP, the little aeroplane, was fed up. He'd been sitting on the tarmac for weeks and weeks. It seemed that nobody wanted to fly him any more.

Once upon a time he used to give pleasure trips at the seaside, with children on board.

"Wheeeee!" they used to shout.

Now it was all quiet, no children, nobody. Then, suddenly, he saw two men walking across the tarmac. Maybe they wanted to fly him! One was tall, with a long beard, the other one small and bouncy, like a ball.

"This is the plane," the tall man said. "You can buy him if you like."

"I'll put him in the museum," the bouncy man said. "He's too old to fly."

"His engine still works," the tall man said. With a quick spin, he turned Champ's propeller round and the engine burst into life.

"This is it!" Champ said to himself. "They're not putting me into a museum."

He pushed himself forward and rolled off down the runway.

"Hey, come back!" the tall man shouted, whose beard was blowing all over his face.

"You can't do that!" the bouncy man screamed, jumping up and down.

"Oh, yes I can," Champ said to himself.

Why couldn't he fly on his own?

His little wheels went faster and faster along the tarmac until his wings lifted him up into the sky and he was away!

CHAMP circled round the airfield and down below he saw the men waving their fists. In the distance, he could see a big river.

"I'll follow that!"

The sun was shining and the river glinted brightly, helping Champ on his way.

He passed over a motorway with cars and lorries streaming along, then over some small villages.

Ahead was a mountain and Champ climbed higher into the sky over the top of the mountain and there, in front of him, was a wonderful sight. The seaside!

A stretch of golden sand went on for miles and miles. The sea rolled lazily into the beach in rippling waves. Champ saw children playing, making sand castles, splashing into the water. He flew low over them and they waved and cheered.

Along the promenade were open-top buses. Champ waggled his wings and some children waved at him from their seats. He wished he could give them a ride in the sky.

"Wheeeeee!" Champ soared away from the promenade and out to sea.

This was better! Down

below he saw some children in a pleasure boat, chugging over the waves. He dipped his wings and they waved. The sea was a lovely deep blue.

Perhaps if he flew on and on, over the sea, he might come to America. Then he remembered. Only the big planes flew to America and he could tell he hadn't very much petrol left. He must get back to the airfield.

HE flew over the mountain, past the villages and along the river. Then he heard his engine coughing.

Oh dear! He was running out of petrol! He must land now. Wasn't that his airfield ahead? Down swooped Champ on to the tarmac, with just enough petrol left.

Champ was tired out after his adventure and went to sleep. He woke up to a crowd of people around him.

"Came down all by himself!" a man said, scratching his head.

"It's a Champ aeroplane," said the nice, kind lady. "Not many of them left."

Champ looked around. This wasn't his airfield. It had lots of other little planes on the tarmac and crowds of people looking at them.

Two boys and a girl were standing with the lady. They liked Champ very much.

"Mummy, can we go up in him?" they asked.

The nice, kind lady smiled. She was a pilot and she promised to take the children up.

Next day, she found where Champ came from and asked the tall man to sell him.

"You can have him," the tall man said. "The museum doesn't want him any more."

The nice, kind lady filled Champ with petrol and the three lucky children climbed inside. She flew Champ over the mountain and right to the seaside.

"Wheeeeee!" the children shouted.

"This is more like it!" Champ said to himself.

And he was so happy with his new family that he never took off on his own again.

Lucy The Toy Lamb

IT was the middle of the night and all the toys were fast asleep in their toy box — all except for Lucy, the woolly lamb.

Lucy couldn't get to sleep. She was worrying because she could only count up to three. After that, the numbers got in a mix, and sometimes seven came before six. Lucy tried again and again, but never got as far as ten.

"I'll ask the Noah's Ark animals to help," she said at last.

She gave a knock. She heard a snore, then two fat pigs came to the door.

"I can't get to sleep," she said. "Something's worrying me."

She told them about the numbers.

"We'll soon sort them out for you, just wait and see," the pigs said.

They fetched the other animals and they all marched round the Noah's Ark, singing this song,

One, two, three, a fidgety flea.
He got stung by a bumble bee.
"Ouch!" he said, and fell in the sea.

Lucy laughed and clapped her hooves.

"What comes next?" she asked. But the animals didn't know any more.

"I'll ask the Jack-in-a-Box," she said.

She called his name, the lid flew up, and out he came.

"I can't get to sleep," said Lucy. "Something's worrying me."

SHE told him about the numbers.

"I'll soon sort them out for you, just wait and see," said the Jack-in-a-Box.

He went back in his box and shut the lid. Then up he sprang. He did it again and again, and he sang this song.

One, two, three, a fidgety flea.
He got stung by a bumble bee.
"Ouch!" he said, and fell in the sea.
Four, five, six, he was in a fix.
But a kind fish from Middlesex
Carried him home, in just two ticks.

Lucy laughed and clapped her hooves.

"What comes next?" she asked. But the Jack-in-a-Box didn't know any more.

"I'll ask the baby doll," said Lucy.

The baby cried.

"Oh, not again!" The Teddy sighed. He picked her up.

"I can't get to sleep," said Lucy. "Something's worrying me."

She told the Teddy bear about the numbers.

"I'll soon sort them out for you, just wait and see," said the Teddy bear.

H E danced round the cradle with the baby doll in his arms, and he sang this song,

*One, two, three, a
fidgety flea.
He got stung by a
bumble bee.*

*"Ouch!" he said, and
fell in the sea.
Four, five, six, he
was in a fix,
But a kind fish from
Middlesex
Carried him home,
in just two ticks.
Seven, eight, nine,*

*the flea was just fine.
Ten, the bee said,
"Sorry", and then
The flea said,
"Please don't do it again."*

Lucy laughed and clapped her hooves.

Just then the toy telephone went brrring-brrring. Lucy counted each ring.

"One, two, three — four, five, six — seven, eight, nine — and TEN!"

"I can do it!" she cried. "I can count to ten!"

Before the telephone could give one more ring Lucy gave a great big yawn and fell fast asleep.

ACTIVITY

CAN YOU COUNT TO 10?

Use the numbers on the page to help you!

83

Dizzy Drew
Goes Shopping

My hat is very shabby,"
Said wizard
Dizzy Drew,
"I'll have to buy
another one,
Yes, that's what
I must do."

He counted out
his savings
To see what he could
spare,
And luckily he had
enough
To buy something
to wear.

He caught the early
morning bus
Into the nearest
town,
And spent a happy
hour or two
Just strolling up
and down.

At last he saw the
perfect shop
With lots of clothes
in view.
He went inside,
and asked if he
Could try a hat
or two.

But then he saw a
lovely suit
In red and orange
flecks.
He bought it, with a
tie to match
In vivid yellow
checks.

He knew his socks were
full of holes,
The worst they'd
ever been.
So bought himself
another pair
In multi-coloured
green.

And then he looked
down at his feet,
And said, "I need new
shoes."
So he bought a pair of
leather pumps
In several different
blues.

Last of all, he bought
a shirt
In darkest indigo,
With violet stripes around
the neck
Ending in a bow.

"My rainbow-coloured
outfit
Should make me look
quite smart,"
Said Dizzy, as he paid
the bill,
Preparing to depart.

Back home he
unpacked all his
things
And laid them
on the bed,
And then he
noticed
something
strange,
And this is what
he said:

"Oh, dear, I am
a ninny —
There is no doubt
about it.
I went to town to
buy a hat
And I've come back
without it!"

KATY KITTEN

KATY the kitten was feeling miserable. Not only was she the only kitten who couldn't miaow — she also didn't even know how to purr properly either!

"I wish I could miaow and purr like all the other cats," Katy said to her mummy one day. "They all seem to be able to do it without even trying!"

Katy's mummy smiled kindly.

"I'm sure you'll soon be able to, Katy," she said. But the little kitten didn't want to have to wait. She wanted to be like everyone else now.

Her best friend, Betsy Bunny, had tried to help.

"Cats only miaow when they become really frightened," she told Katy. "Perhaps if someone scares you — that might make you miaow."

Katy thought it was worth a try.

"But how can I become frightened?" she asked.

Betsy Bunny had a plan.

"Hannah Hare and I will jump out at you when you're not looking. That will give you a fright! We'll go to the park and try it today."

So off they all went. Katy's two friends jumped out at her from behind the trees. Then they popped up out of the badger holes to surprise her again!

"Boo!" they called out to the small kitten.

But Katy wasn't at all scared. In fact, she thought it was all quite funny.

"How can I be scared of that?" She laughed out loud. Then, when Hannah made a funny face, she laughed even more.

"This is supposed to be a horrible face to frighten you!" Hannah giggled, grimacing. Then she glanced at her reflection in a puddle and laughed, too.

By the end of the week, Katy still hadn't learnt how to miaow or purr.

"I'm sure it'll happen very soon now," her mummy said. "In the meantime, why don't we go for a walk in the wood?"

Katy thought that was a lovely idea. It was a warm, sunny day and all the bluebells were out.

"Katy — don't run off!" her mummy called, as the young kitten scampered on ahead. Katy didn't listen. She was too busy collecting wild flowers.

MUMMY — look at these!" she called. She turned around, clutching a bunch of bluebells, but her mummy was nowhere to be seen! The little kitten hadn't realised she'd wandered so far into the wood.

Suddenly, she felt quite lost and alone.

What shall I do, she thought. Then, without knowing how it happened, Katy let out the biggest miaow you ever heard!

86

MIAAAAOOOOW, miaaaow, miaaow, miaaaaaow!"

Katy's mummy came running towards her from the trees. She looked very surprised indeed.

"Katy — was that you?" she gasped in wonder.

Katy nodded. She could hardly believe it herself.

"It was me," she replied. "I thought I was lost. I miaowed to call you — all by myself!"

"I always knew if you really needed to miaow, you could."

Her mummy smiled. "But you weren't lost — you just couldn't see me behind the trees!"

Katy was very proud. She practised her miaowing all the way home.

"I hope you're not going to cry like that all day," her mummy joked. She had walked back with her paws over her ears!

When Betsy Bunny and Hannah Hare heard her, they could hardly believe their ears either.

"Goodness me!" They laughed. "What a big miaow for such a little kitten!"

Katy's mummy smiled. "I think that's enough noise for one day," she said. "It's your bedtime, too!" she told the kitten.

KATY got ready for bed. She had never felt happier. She snuggled down under the covers quietly to go to sleep.

But, suddenly she heard a strange noise. It was a soft, gentle, contented, kind of noise . . .

"Purr, purr, purr!"

"Mummy!" she called quickly. "Listen — it's me — I've learned how to purr."

Katy's mummy laughed.

"I told you it would happen soon," she told the delighted kitten. "And, of course, it did!"

And Katy smiled to herself as she settled down to sleep.

ACTIVITY

LOOK AT KATY'S COLOURFUL PATCHWORK QUILT!

Can you name all the colours?

87

D AVID, his little sister, Amy, Mummy and Daddy had moved to a new house.

But there was a problem. There was a large bedroom, a middle-sized bedroom and a tiny bedroom with space for only a bed, a little table and a chair.

Nobody wanted the tiny room. Mummy and Daddy, of course, had to have the large bedroom for there were two of them. But who was to have the small room, David or Amy?

"We'll toss a coin," Daddy said. "Heads, you have the small room, Amy. Tails, David gets it."

The coin came down with tails uppermost.

"You get the tiny room, David," Mummy said. "I'm sure you'll get to like it."

"I won't have much space to do much!" David grumbled. "No room for my train set."

"You may play in my room," Amy told him.

"Thanks, Amy," David said, but he felt disappointed.

Why, the tiny room didn't even have a proper window, only one up in the roof, and you could see only the sky through it.

The bed had been made specially to fit the tiny room,

ACTIVITY

LOOK AT THE CLOUDS IN THE PICTURE.

What shapes can you see?

DAVID'S ROOM

and was high off the floor. Indeed, it was so high, David had to climb a little ladder to get on to it.

Underneath the bed was a dark place into which David found he could crawl. He could sit quite comfortably in there.

This is a nice, secret place, David thought. He crawled out, found a book and a torch, and went back in.

In the dark, secret place, he read by torchlight.

When he'd finished reading, he thought, this dark place is just right for showing films.

So, he fetched his toy projector and film strips of Pooh Bear and his friends. He asked Amy to come and they both crawled under the high bed and had a picture show.

GRANDMA peeped into the secret place.

"You are lucky, David, having this little room," she said. "Not only do you have a secret place but, instead of a window, you have a skylight," and she pointed to the window in the roof.

David and Amy looked up, and saw a bird fly past the skylight.

"Did you spot which bird that was?" Grandma asked.

"No, it flew past too quickly," David replied.

"It was a black-headed gull," Grandma told him. "We'll have to look at your bird book and get to know how the different birds look. Then, you'll be able to bird-watch through your skylight and tell which birds fly past."

LATER that day, they watched clouds through the skylight, and noticed that some were shaped like castles, some like animals and some like strange faces.

"This is fun," Amy said.

When David lay in bed that night, he looked up at the dark blue night sky studded with sparkling, silver stars, till his eyes closed and he fell asleep.

And, when he woke up in the morning, the first thing he did was look up at his skylight. What a surprise he got! The skylight was covered with ferny, leafy patterns.

"What's happened to my skylight?" David asked Mummy.

"Jack Frost has drawn an ice picture on it," Mummy explained. "Enjoy it before the sun comes and melts it away."

David ran for Amy, so that she could see Jack Frost's picture.

"Lucky you, David, to have this tiny room," Amy said.

"Yes," David said with a smile. "I think it must be the most interesting room in the house!" And Amy agreed.

THE WITCH WHO SWITCHED

INSIDE her hollow tree home, Witch stirred tricks and magic spells in a big pot as Puss watched from his corner.

Suddenly she threw her big spoon on the floor.

"Puss!" she croaked. "It's almost Hallowe'en and the forest folk will be planning their party. I've always played tricks on them, but I'm tired of doing that, Puss. I'm so lonely I wish they would be my friends.

"I'll give a party in the forest and invite them all. I'll show them I can be a nice, friendly witch." She reached for her black cape and tall hat.

"Come on, Puss, let's go and tell them."

But when the animals and birds saw them coming, they scattered away to hide.

"I'm giving a party!" she called out. "Everybody's invited. Please come! I want to be your friend."

ACTIVITY

CAN YOU SPOT THE THREE LITTLE PUMPKINS ON THESE PAGES?

ON/OFF

90

"What's going on?" they chattered. "What is she plotting? A party? No! It's a trick. Don't listen to her!"

Disappointed, Witch trudged back home with Puss.

"They don't trust me. How can I show them I mean no harm?"

IN the middle of the night she sat up in her straw bed.

"Puss," she called. "We're going to see Mr Wise Owl."

Puss stretched and followed Witch as she hobbled with her crooked cane into the dark woods.

From his perch in the tall tree, the owl greeted her politely. Witch told him she wanted to be a kind witch, but the forest folk wouldn't believe her.

"I invited them to a party, but they all ran away," she said.

"I'll help," the wise old bird said, "but only if you promise you will never again tease the forest folk."

"I will be good. I'm tired of being mean," Witch promised.

"Come back tomorrow after dark," he said.

The next night Witch and Puss sat in the big oak tree in the silent forest, watching as spiders in a corner spun miles of silk thread.

Mr Wise Owl pulled it in his beak over to his wife, who knitted and sewed. At dawn, Witch tried on the new clothes.

Her gnarled fingers smoothed the soft dress Mrs Wise Owl had made from cobwebs with flower petals and a belt of green ivy. She wore a silvery cobweb shawl, not her black cape. Instead of the black pointed hat she wore one made of bluebird feathers.

Puss stared and grinned.

Next day, Witch made sweets in her black cauldron that bubbled with syrup instead of magic potions.

AT last it was the day of the party. Before daylight Witch and Puss crept across the silent meadow.

She set out toffee apples and cakes and lots of tasty things on a flat rock. Then she sat down to wait.

Soon she saw Mr and Mrs Wise Owl leading a crowd of forest creatures towards her.

"Close your eyes. Get ready for a surprise!" Mr Wise Owl said. They stood still, wings and paws covering their faces. "Now! Open your eyes. Witch and Puss are waiting for you. She is giving a party this Hallowe'en."

Witch heard them nervously chattering among themselves.

"Is it really Witch? She looks so nice. She's not scary."

"Yes, it's really me. I'm sorry for all the mean tricks I've played and I want to change my ways. Will you be my friends?" she said.

But the animals and birds were still not sure.

"Don't be afraid!" Mr Wise Owl said. "Come along, let's enjoy her party. She promised me she'll be nice to you from now on."

They moved forward and Witch greeted them. Then everyone had a wonderful party.

Finally, the animals said goodbye and told Witch and Puss to come and play in the forest the next day.

Witch said she would love to and Puss purred loudly. Then Witch turned and thanked Mr and Mrs Wise Owl for their kind help.

This, she thought, is the best Hallowe'en fun I've ever had!

DAD says, "It's bedtime, Billy Bear! Let's clean your teeth and brush your hair." But Billy's taking far too long — He won't put his pyjamas on.

············ ⬭ ············

"You'll have to catch me first!" he cries And out the bathroom door he flies. He runs out in his birthday suit — Dad follows him in hot pursuit.

Upstairs and downstairs, round the house, He scares the cat and shocks a mouse. Poor old Dad, he's feeling dizzy — Mum's puffed out and in a tizzy.

············ ⬭ ············

Dad yawns! "With all this rushing about I'm feeling tired and quite worn out!" "Me, too!" Mum sighs and nods her head. "Let's us two go to bed instead."

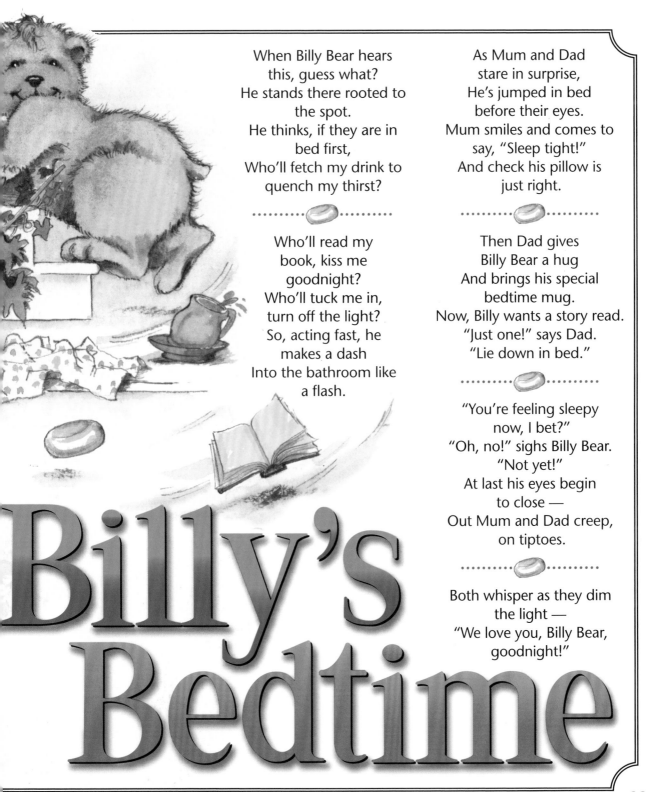

When Billy Bear hears
this, guess what?
He stands there rooted to
the spot.
He thinks, if they are in
bed first,
Who'll fetch my drink to
quench my thirst?

Who'll read my
book, kiss me
goodnight?
Who'll tuck me in,
turn off the light?
So, acting fast, he
makes a dash
Into the bathroom like
a flash.

As Mum and Dad
stare in surprise,
He's jumped in bed
before their eyes.
Mum smiles and comes to
say, "Sleep tight!"
And check his pillow is
just right.

Then Dad gives
Billy Bear a hug
And brings his special
bedtime mug.
Now, Billy wants a story read.
"Just one!" says Dad.
"Lie down in bed."

"You're feeling sleepy
now, I bet?"
"Oh, no!" sighs Billy Bear.
"Not yet!"
At last his eyes begin
to close —
Out Mum and Dad creep,
on tiptoes.

Both whisper as they dim
the light —
"We love you, Billy Bear,
goodnight!"

Billy's Bedtime

MR GALE FORCE WIND

MR GALE FORCE WIND was in a brisk mood! He told the leaves it would soon be time for him to blow them off the trees.

"You have all enjoyed a lovely summer!" he said. "Plenty of sunshine, gentle rain and, of course, my friend!

"Now the air is getting chilly. Autumn is here and I shall be busy all over the country, scattering the leaves to their new surroundings, then I will return to deal with this forest load! Be ready, please . . . !" And Mr Gale Force Wind blew himself away!

ALL the leaves, but one, were excited at thoughts of new surroundings. Where would they settle down?

Some would land no farther than at the foot of their own trees! Others would be carried away on the wind and tossed into the fields.

Some would be swept along in the stream, or find a cosy home in hedgerows, or under bridges. One leaf, though, wanted to stay on its bough, no matter how hard Mr Gale Force Wind tried to blow it away.

The little leaf began to sway madly, to and fro!

Leaves scattered in all directions, some settling down, only to be scooped up again, and blown farther away. Mr Gale Force Wind was very energetic!

Soon all the leaves were gone, except for the one little leaf.

Mr Gale Force Wind had also gone, so all was quiet. Very chilly, too! The bare trees stretched away, like a tunnel, and all along the forest they created quite a draught.

THE little leaf was cold as evening drew on, and wished now it had been blown away with the others. How could it escape from the bough, without Mr Gale Force Wind's help?

Suddenly Mr Gale Force Wind returned, exhausted, rather less gale force than a light breeze! He was having a last look around to see no leaves remained on the tree. He spotted the only one clinging to the bough!

"Goodness me!" he exclaimed. "Fancy you still here! I wonder how I missed you? Don't think I've got enough puff left."

He blew and he blew, but it was a feeble effort. He'd been so busy elsewhere.

The little leaf hoped he would try again. It longed to be safely settled somewhere.

"It's no good!" Mr Gale Force Wind gasped, out of breath. "I simply must have a rest, and try again later."

He disappeared, and the little leaf shivered. How much longer to wait?

Time passed then, W-H-O-O-S-H, the little leaf found himself flying through the air up, up, over the trees — still flying! Mr Gale Force Wind dropped it gently, to nestle in among the reeds by the bridge.

How glad he was to have a new home, and to be with some of his friends. They all had a good laugh about Mr Gale Force Wind being out of breath. Wasn't it a relief, that he managed to blow the little leaf off the bough, at last . . . ?

The Little Blue Tractor

CHUG, chug, chug! Little Blue Tractor worked his way steadily around the hillside. Farmer Jones steered him over the humps and bumps, around the big oak tree and down to the barn.

There, with a last wheezy chug-a-chug, the tractor stopped. Another day's work was done.

Little Blue Tractor was tired. His tyres were worn and his paint was scratched and rusty.

Every day, the farmer found it harder to start the tractor's engine. Every day poor Little Blue Tractor found it harder to huff and puff his way around the farm.

Once, he had been a proud new tractor with shiny paint and a powerful engine. How hard he had worked for the farmer then.

"We make a good team,"

the farmer would boast, when people stopped to admire Little Blue Tractor.

But that was all a long time ago.

THEN, one day, a big truck came up the road to the farm. There, on the truck, was the biggest, newest tractor you ever would see.

Its red paint gleamed in the sun, its tyres were huge, and there was a glassed-in, air-conditioned cabin where the driver could sit.

Everyone fussed over the big new tractor, examining the gears and levers and listening to the roar of the engine. Little Blue Tractor stood alone and forgotten.

As the weeks passed, the smart new tractor worked its way up and down the hills without one little puff or wheeze.

Soon, Little Blue Tractor's paint was covered in dust. Spiders' webs dangled from his steering wheel and one of the farm hens had made a

nest on his rusty seat.

One afternoon, a truck pulled up outside the barn. Farmer Jones started up Little Blue Tractor's engine and backed him out of the barn. He drove him up a ramp and on to the truck.

"Did you think I was going to leave you in the barn until you fell to pieces?" the farmer said to Little Blue Tractor.

"You have been a good and faithful friend, and you deserve better than that."

Before long, the truck with Little Blue Tractor was bumping away down the road. The farm was left far behind.

It was almost dark when they stopped. Once more, Little Blue Tractor's engine was started. He was backed down the ramp and into a big shed.

EARLY the next morning, the shed door was thrown open. Bright sunlight flooded in.

Little Blue Tractor's new

owner ran his hands over the rusty paintwork.

"You are a bit of a mess, old thing," he said, "but we'll soon have you looking as good as new."

His hands were gentle as he rubbed away the rusty old paint. Then he painted Little Blue Tractor a bright blue with sunshiny yellow tyres. He gave him a new steering wheel and a new seat.

How wonderful and smart Little Blue Tractor looked, and how proud he was.

They took him to a children's playground where he now sits in a sunny place near the swings and roundabouts.

Every day children come to play. They climb up into the driver's seat and drive Little Blue Tractor up and

down pretend hills. They make loud chugging noises, just like his engine used to make.

The children laugh as they climb all over Little Blue Tractor's sunshiny yellow tyres. How happy they are.

But the happiest of all is . . . Can you guess? Little Blue Tractor. How proud and special he feels.

Star Fairies

STAR fairies flying through the air,
All dressed in silvery white,
With stardust sprinkled in their hair
To catch the moon's bright light.

Old Father Moon shines up there still,
Beaming big and bold,
Through summer nights and winter's chill,
He's very, very old!

Little moonbeams dance around
And with the fairies play.
On starry, moonlit nights they're found,
But vanish with the day.

Sometimes, across the cool night air
A star goes shooting by.
It's in a hurry getting there —
We don't know where or why.

If you wish upon a star,
Your wishes may come true.
It doesn't matter where you are,
The star is there for you.

Star fairies take their lanterns bright
Along the Milky Way
And touch each star with silvery light.
They shine till break of day.

They glitter in the midnight sky,
Like diamonds in the blue,
Then fairies sing a lullaby
And bring their dreams to you.

Moonbeams dance and fairies fly
While all the earth's asleep,
And big old moon 'way up on high
His nightly watch will keep.

And stars will twinkle through
the night —
Bright jewels overhead —
Shining with the moon's clear light
O'er every sleepy head.

The Perfect Present

EARLY one morning, Baby Squirrel left his cosy nest high in a hole in the tree and went to look for a birthday present for Mummy Squirrel.

He looked very hard, but he couldn't find anything.

Slowly, the sun slid up over the trees. Baby Squirrel saw some smooth, shiny things lying on the ground.

"They're acorns," Big Sister Squirrel said.

"They look almost too good to eat," Baby Squirrel said. "I'll save them for a special treat."

Then he had an idea — the acorns would make a perfect birthday present.

Baby Squirrel hid them in a safe place while he did his morning exercises. Afterwards he went to fetch them.

Suddenly, he stopped. He gave a little cry.

Baby Squirrel couldn't remember where he had put the acorns.

He ran round in a tizzy, and made himself dizzy.

"I've lost my acorns!" he cried. "What shall I do?"

"Stand on your head at the top of the tree," Big Sister Squirrel said. "That is the method that works well for me."

Baby Squirrel hurried helter-shelter up the tree. He stood on his head and blinked through the branches.

He saw a nest full of birds. They opened their beaks and made a fuss.

"Have you brought some breakfast for us?" they asked.

Baby Squirrel jumped into the nest. The birds squeezed up tight and nearly popped out.

"My acorns aren't here," Baby Squirrel said. He chattered and made such a din that soon his head began to spin.

"I've lost my acorns! What shall I do?" he cried.

"Sit up on a high branch and wave your long tail," Daddy Squirrel said. "For me that's the method that works without fail."

Baby Squirrel leaped lickety-split on to a high branch.

He waved his long tail and looked through the leaves.

He saw a nest full of wasps. They zoomed busily about and went zing-zing.

"Look in here if you like," they said. "But mind we don't sting."

BABY SQUIRREL stuck his head in the nest. The wasps whizzed out like a yellow striped cloud.

"My acorns aren't here," Baby Squirrel said. He leaped from branch to branch with hardly a pause.

"Careless jumping! You'll go tumbling!" Mummy Squirrel said.

"I've lost my acorns! What shall I do? I haven't got a present for you."

"Run down the tree and look on the ground," Mummy Squirrel said. "That is the method that works best, I've found."

100

Baby Squirrel hurry-scurried head first down the tree and looked all around. He saw a mole peering out of a hole.

The mole waved both his black claws in the air.

"Come and look in my home," he said. "You've tried looking up there."

BABY SQUIRREL climbed down the hole. He couldn't see his acorns anywhere. He gave a big sigh and sat down for a rest, but he couldn't get comfortable. He squiggled and squirmed.

"Why are you wriggling like a worm?" the mole asked.

"I'm sitting on something lumpy-bumpy," Baby Squirrel said. "It feels just like . . ." Quickly, he jumped up. He looked down and there were his acorns!

"I remember now!" he cried. "I buried them!"

The mole helped him to pick them up and Baby Squirrel took them home as fast as he could.

Mummy Squirrel said it was the best birthday present she'd ever had.

101

ACTIVITY

THERE ARE SIX ACORNS HIDDEN AROUND THESE PAGES.

Can you spot them all?

THE FIR TREE'S SPECIAL TIME

IN James and Carly's garden there stood a big old beech tree and a little young fir tree.

Spring came, the leaf buds opened into soft, smooth, pale green leaves, and birds made their nests among them.

"How lovely you look, and how useful you are," the fir tree said to the beech tree. Then it sighed. "My leaves are like sharp needles and the birds don't come to nest among them. I wish I were like you."

"By and by, you'll be pretty and useful, too," the beech said.

"When will that be?" the fir wondered.

"Be patient. Wait and see," the beech said.

Summer came. The days were sunny and hot. Mummy put a table and chairs beneath the leafy beech tree, and she, James, Carly and Daddy had their meals in its shade.

"Isn't it cool and pleasant beneath this fine old tree?" Mummy asked.

"Yes, we're lucky to have it!" Daddy and James and Carly all agreed.

ACTIVITY

ONE, TWO, THREE ... LET'S SEE IF YOU CAN COUNT ALL THE BAUBLES ON THE FIR TREE.

When the family went back into the house, the little fir felt sadder than ever.

"How proud you must be to please the family so much," it said to the beech tree.

"There'll be a time when you'll be the one who'll please them very much, and make them happy," the beech said kindly.

In the autumn, the leaves of the beech became golden and brown, and it was covered with nuts which the family called beech-mast. Squirrels scampered happily all over the old tree, cracking the nut cases, crunching the nuts inside, and hiding some away in their stores for winter.

"There you are, useful again," the fir said. "I'm no use for anything."

"Cheer up, it won't be long now till you will be very useful," the beech said.

Next came winter and with it strong winds that tore the leaves off the beech. Soon its branches were bare.

"Goodnight, little fir," the kind beech said. "I'm going to snooze till spring, but be sure to give me a shout when anything exciting happens to you. I don't want to miss your special time."

"What's going to happen to me?" the fir asked, but the beech tree was asleep.

"Oh, well, I'll just have to wait and see," the little fir murmured to itself.

THEN, one day, snowflakes came drifting down from dark grey clouds. Soon all over the garden lay soft, white snow. James and Carly made a snowman, and cleared a path to the front door.

One afternoon, the whole family came down the path to where the little fir stood.

Carly carried a box and James brought an electricity cable. Carly took fairy lights out of the box, and she and Mummy arranged them over the fir tree. Daddy attached the special outdoor cable.

"Now, push down the switch, James," Daddy said.

James did and there was the fir tree all aglow with fairy lights.

"The fir looks beautiful," Mummy said.

"It's the prettiest Christmas tree we've ever had," Carly said.

The little fir tree stood as straight and tall as it could. It felt very proud and happy.

"Beech tree," it called. "Wake up. It's happened."

"What did I tell you?" The beech smiled. "Now you're beautiful, useful, and making the family very pleased. Wasn't it worth waiting for? Enjoy every minute of being a Christmas tree."

"I will," the little fir said. And it did.

A HAPPY MEMORY

IT was Tuesday afternoon at Fairview School. The early November winds had blown nearly all the leaves off the big tree outside Class 1.

"Time to tidy up, children," Mrs May said. "It's circle time!

"Now then!" Mrs May smiled. "I'm going to tell you all about festivals that happen in other parts of the world!

"We'll begin with 'Diwali', the Hindu festival of light, which is celebrated in India at the end of October or early November."

Sophie felt very excited. Her great-grandmother had grown up in India and had told her wonderful stories about what it had been like to live there.

Granny Mary, as Sophie called her, lived in a nursing home, and it was fun to visit her and look through her album of old photographs.

Sophie's favourite was a picture of Granny Mary as a little girl, standing in front of the most magnificent palace in India, the Taj Mahal.

There was also a picture of an elephant, painted in swirling designs with ropes of jewels round his head.

"Did you ever ride on an elephant, Granny Mary?" Sophie had asked.

"Oh, yes!" She'd smiled. She was very old, but her bright blue eyes still sparkled. "It was very comfortable!"

SOPHIE remembered the photograph as Mrs May told the children all about Diwali, when Hindus hold a festival for Vishnu.

"He is one of their most important gods. He looks after the world, and the Hindus believe that he came to earth in

104

ACTIVITY

IN THIS STORY SOPHIE'S GRANNY SHARES HER MEMORIES.

Your grandma and grandad were little once, too. Ask them to share a special memory with you.

different forms.

"Once, he came as a prince, called Rama, who went away on a long quest.

"So, to show him the way home, the Hindus light little oil lamps and put them by their doors and windows and on boats. The lamps are little clay dishes called 'diwas' and, that's why they call the festival 'Diwali'.

"They eat special food and wear necklaces made of flowers.

"We're going to make flower necklaces and diwas in class this week!"

The children were all very excited, and, on the way home from school, Sophie had a wonderful idea. She couldn't wait to tell her mother about it.

All week, Sophie and the children made necklaces of paper flowers and diwas out of clay.

ON Saturday evening, just as it was getting dark, Sophie packed up a carrier bag and she and her mother went to the nursing home.

"Good evening!" the nurse said. "Your Granny Mary is in the television room at the moment."

Sophie's mother went to find her and Sophie hurried to her bedroom.

She took out the diwas she had made and placed them on the window-sill, dressing-table and bedside table.

Then, she went to find the nurse, who kindly lit the candles which Sophie had put into the diwas. They switched off the lights.

The little flames flickered like stars and it looked like a glittering fairyland.

"Shall I ask them to come in now?" asked the nurse.

"Yes, please!" Sophie answered. Then the door opened and Granny Mary stepped in.

She just stood and gazed into the glowing room.

"Oh, Sophie, darling . . . it's Diwali!" she whispered.

Sophie put necklaces of flowers round her mother and Granny Mary, and gave them each a hug. Then they all sat on the bed and watched the dancing candlelight as Granny Mary told them stories about Diwali.

"I feel like we've been taken to India — by magic!" Sophie said.

"So do I," said Granny Mary. "Thank you for bringing happy memories of India back to me."

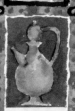

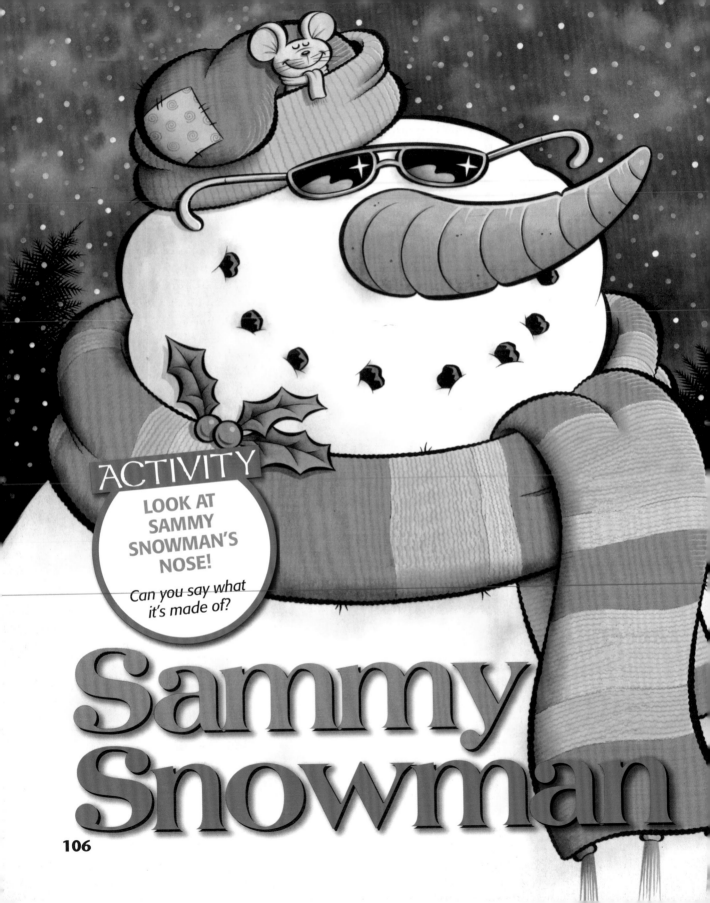

ACTIVITY

LOOK AT
SAMMY
SNOWMAN'S
NOSE!

*Can you say what
it's made of?*

Sammy
Snowman

SAMMY SNOWMAN had had a lovely day. The children living nearby had come out into the snowy meadow especially to play with him.

He'd been given a huge carrot nose, potato buttons down his front and a lovely woolly hat and scarf to wear.

"What fun we've had!" Sammy smiled to himself, remembering.

But now it was night-time. All the children were home in bed, fast asleep.

The snow fell thickly in the meadow and Sammy shivered, although it wasn't from the cold.

"Oh, I feel so lonely out here by myself." He sighed. "I wish the children were here with me right now."

Poor Sammy had a long wait — morning was hours away. Meanwhile he tried hard to sleep, but just couldn't.

The wind was howling through the trees, keeping him awake and Sammy felt a tiny bit scared.

Just then he heard a really loud rustling nearby.

"W-who's that?" Sammy stammered.

"Hello, it's only me," replied Morris Mouse. "I'm sorry I made you jump, but I wanted to ask you a favour."

Sammy was puzzled.

"What kind of favour?" he asked.

Morris explained that he'd like to sleep inside Sammy's woolly hat.

"It looks so lovely and warm — and I'm so terribly cold." Morris shivered.

Sammy was pleased to help.

"Climb up," he told Morris.

A little later, Sammy was still having trouble sleeping — despite hearing Morris's comforting snores coming from his hat.

He couldn't believe his eyes when Sherry Shrew came along next.

"Excuse me," Sherry piped up to Sammy. "I'm sorry to disturb you so late at night, but I wanted to ask you a favour."

It turned out that Sherry hadn't found any food that day because of the heavy snow. She was starving — and hoped for a nibble of Sammy's carrot nose.

"I won't eat much," Sherry promised. "Just enough to stop my tummy from rumbling."

SAMMY didn't mind at all.

"My nose is too big anyway." He chuckled.

"Besides, the children can always find me another one in the morning."

So, after eating, Sherry snuggled up in the folds of Sammy's scarf. Soon she was snoring away, too.

The only trouble was that Sammy still couldn't sleep himself — so he decided to tell himself a story in the hope that it might help him drop off.

"Once upon a time there was a little snowman . . ."

Sammy began his story, but suddenly stopped in surprise.

He wasn't sure where she'd come from, but Natalie Nightingale had flown across and landed in front of him.

"You're up late," Natalie trilled. "Can I ask you a favour? Can you tell your bedtime story to me, please — I can't sleep."

SAMMY chuckled and carried on, with Natalie perched on his shoulder.

By the time he'd finished, the little bird had fallen asleep and was snoring loudly, too!

Sammy gave a big yawn — but he was still wide awake. Then, it suddenly struck him.

He wasn't alone in the meadow any more. He had Morris and Sherry and now even Natalie to keep him company.

So, with a happy smile, Sammy finally closed his eyes and soon slept as soundly as all his new friends.

And do you know what? There was no-one left awake to check if he snored loudly, too!

IT was the night
before Christmas
And, at the North Pole,
There was a panic!
Santa's sleigh
Had a big gaping hole.

Santa's cries could be heard
All across the cold north,
And his whole workshop
shook
As he stomped back and
forth.

He ranted and raved
And he fumed and he
fussed.
"It's late and I must
Take the toys down. I
MUST!"

Space
Age Santa

"This is dreadful!" he roared.
"All the small girls and boys
Will wake Christmas
morning
And look for their toys."

He moaned and he groaned.
"My big night of the year
And my broken-down sleigh
Keeps me stranded
up here."

"Now, dear," his wife
soothed.
"Don't get so upset.
We'll think of some way
To get you there yet."

Just then a sleek rocket
Whizzed past at great speed.
"Look, look!" Mrs Claus
squealed.
"That's just what you need."

Santa called on his
telephone.
"SOS! SOS!
Is that space headquarters?"
A voice answered, "Yes?"

"Hello, this is Santa.
I can't use my sleigh
And the children are
waiting.
I need help right away."

"Now, Santa!" the
voice said.
"There's no need to worry.
We'll send you a spaceship.
Get ready, now, hurry!"

In a flash it flew near them
And Santa Claus waved.
His wife and the elves
clapped.
"Oh, Santa, you're saved."

The spaceship came lower,
Above them it stopped
And Santa looked up
As a silk ladder dropped.

With sacks on his back,
Santa grabbed for a rung,
But his legs dangled down
And he twisted and swung.

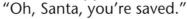

He was red-faced and
puffing,
Growing madder and
madder,
Then, with one last
attempt,
He was climbing the ladder.

"Oh, please, do be careful,"
Mrs Claus then implored,
As an astronaut reached
And pulled Santa
on board.

Through a porthole he
waved
As he vanished from sight,
Flying faster than sound
As they raced through
the night.

They zipped and they
zoomed
Past the Milky Way stars.
"Be careful," begged
Santa.
"Don't bump into Mars!"

As quick as a star wink
Santa left all the toys
Around the whole world
For sleeping girls
and boys.

Now, if you had wakened
And peeked at the sky,
You'd have seen that
sleek spaceship
Go swish-swooping by.

But, would you have
guessed,
For even one minute,
That old Santa Claus
And your presents were
in it?

I DIP into my
paint-box
With my brush so
long and thin,
I think that I'll use
Red to start.
Now, where shall I begin?

An apple tree, a post-box,
A cherry, and a rose —
If I keep well between
the lines,
I'll soon do all of those!

Now I'll dip my
brush in Blue,
And make a sea and sky,
And next I'll paint
a bluebird
That's flying up so high.

After that, I wash
my brush
To make it nice
and clean,
Before I have
another go,
And start again
with Green.

Green takes brushes
full of paint,
There's so much grass
and trees,
It means a lot of
work for me
To finish all of these!

Yellow makes nice
golden sand,
And then a smiling sun.
A wizard's cloak has
yellow stars,
So yellow is quite fun!

Purple is for kings
and queens,
Or any things I choose —
For aeroplanes, and
elephants,
For funny hats,
and shoes.

So now I've finished
painting,
My hands are washed
and clean,
And Mummy says
my pictures
Are quite the best
she's seen!

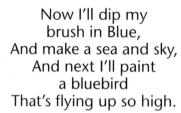

PAINTING PICTURES